Beyond Courage

Based on Historical Events

David Lee Corley

DEDICATION

To all the men and women that fought for their country.
Your sacrifices will be remembered.

Table of Contents

OPERATION MARAUDER.................................6

COURT AT THE CARAVELLE.......................22

KEYMAN...35

OPERATION VAN BUREN 48

WHITE WING 66

BATTLES OF NA KHANG 104

DOPE...118

THE STRUGGLE 147

ARC LIGHT...172

PAUL REVERE 179

TEN YEARS OF CHAOS...............................184

ALLIES 205

BATON ROUGE...233

THE YELLOW PARROT...............................257

THAYER AND IRVING 266

OPERATION SEA DRAGON.........................283

LETTER TO THE READER 318

LIST OF TITLES WITH READING ORDER ...319

AUTHOR'S BIOGRAPHY.............................321

"I hate war as only a soldier who has lived it can, only as one who has seen its brutality, its futility, its stupidity."

Dwight D. Eisenhower

OPERATION MARAUDER

January 1, 1966 - Mekong Delta, South Vietnam

As dawn broke a squadron of Bell UH-1 Iroquois helicopters known as "slicks" swept across a vast wetland reflecting the fiery cloud-pocked sky. The armada was carrying US, Australian, New Zealander, and ARVN forces. It was flanked by cobra gunships and led by scout helicopters known as "loaches." Tandem rotor, heavy-lift CH-47 Chinooks with under-fuselage slings carrying artillery would follow in the second flight.

The endless swamp they were flying over was the Plain of Reeds. It was mostly treeless and flatter than a pancake. The only place to hide was within the reeds that covered much of the swamp. It wasn't great cover, but it did the job when a soldier needed to disappear. It hadn't rained in almost a week and the ground was still wet as far as the eye could see. It was the dry season in the Mekong Delta which meant no afternoon rain to take the edge off the heat of the day.

Viet Cong 506th and 267th Battalions called the Plain of Reeds their home. They were the target of Operation Marauder – a joint taskforce made up of the

US 173rd Airborne Brigade, 1st Battalion, Royal Australian Regiment, and 161st Battery, Royal New Zealand Artillery. The American commander of the task force was Brigadier General Ellis Williamson. It was the first time US forces had operated in the area and the Americans were itching to prove their steel.

Rene Granier, a veteran soldier and CIA officer, and a team of ten would-be snipers rode in a Huey piloted by Lieutenant Scott Dickson, his friend Tom Coyle's son. Granier liked Scott and thought he was a good soldier, professional and focused.

Except for the first round of insertions, which required all available transports, Scott had been assigned to Granier and his students for the duration of the operation. He felt like Granier's on-call chauffeur but didn't gripe about it. It wouldn't have done any good anyway. Granier was a respected veteran doing MACV a favor. He got whatever he requested except for more time to train his men. With a mile-long backlog of newly trained snipers, more training time just wasn't in the cards.

The student snipers were broken up into five teams, each with a spotter and a sniper. After his previous success training South Vietnamese snipers, MACV asked him to head up a crash course to rapidly train ARVN snipers. Granier didn't like heading up anything. He was a warrior that liked fighting alone whenever possible. However, he did like the idea of passing on some of the skills he had learned over the years. He also recognized the need for more snipers in the ARVN forces. After his commander in the CIA had approved MACV's request, Granier had little choice but to accept the assignment and began putting together the program. The first batch of snipers was riding with him. They had already completed two weeks of training in the classroom and on the firing range. Now was the field test and hopefully graduation from the program. Granier knew that he couldn't train a real sniper in just a few weeks. That would take at least a year and would require months in the field. These guys were something else – like shake-and-bake snipers. They would be spread around the ARVN forces and give their commanders a weapon that they didn't currently process. It was sloppy and rushed in his opinion, but so were a lot of things in Vietnam. ARVN commanders constantly stomped out fires that they had created. It was ridiculous at times. It was reality.

Granier planned to set up the crash course sniper program, crank out the first couple of batches of students, then turn it over to someone else and move on to another assignment. The problem was that if the program was successful, MACV might request that he take the position permanently. If that happened and the CIA complied with MACV's request, Granier would resign. He wasn't going to be forced into doing anything he didn't want to do. He wasn't sure what he would do after his service in Vietnam. It gave him an uneasy feeling but so did playing schoolmarm. He couldn't bring himself to sabotage the program so MACV would release him. Granier was a patriot and would do what was necessary to protect his country, even in this faraway land of chaos. He would do his best to develop an effective sniper program and let the chips fall where they may.

Lieutenant Dickson and three other pilots from his

squadron were on temporary assignment to the transportation company taking the soldiers into battle. Four pilots that had served a year in Vietnam had been rotated back to the states just before the mission.

As he flew one of the troop carriers, Scott wondered about the wisdom of releasing pilots from service after only one year of combat duty. It seemed like it took a year before a pilot got the hang of flying in combat. Unit cohesion, combat experience, and competent leadership marked the difference between victory and defeat. The Army's rotation policy made little sense to those who lived through it. Helicopter pilots were sent home just as they became useful. Many agreed with Scott's thinking. But once the US military codified a policy it would take an act of God to get the generals at the Pentagon to change it.

For officers to advance in rank, they needed combat experience. Vietnam offered that opportunity to those that wanted it. There was no shortage of volunteers to command troops in the field. The rotation of officers created more opportunities to gain battlefield experience. The US military needed a vast stable of veteran commanders in case a larger war broke out in Europe or elsewhere. Rotation made sense to the wonks and generals in the Pentagon.

His attention snapped back to the job at hand but then faded looking out at the green carpet before him. He thought about Coyle, his newfound father. Although it wasn't easy, Scott had overcome his feelings of guilt toward the man that raised him, Colonel Dickson. He now knew he wasn't betraying him by having a relationship with Coyle, his real father. The colonel had taught him many things about being a man and commitment to duty and honor. He would never forget those ideals. They were part of him now. But Coyle had other things to teach him. Things he needed to learn to survive the Nam. He had just rejoined for another tour. He felt it would have been hypocrisy to do otherwise. Coyle was a nature flying and trusted his instincts more than the flight officer's manual. He took calculated risks and always seemed to come out on top. Scott wanted that for himself. He wanted to be a better pilot. He never came out and asked Coyle directly for advice. But the few times he had seen Coyle fly had saved his life. Coyle was a true warrior and a father that protected his son. For that, Scott was grateful. He tried to show his gratitude with small gestures, but it wasn't easy for him. Scott was proud. Maybe that was part of what he needed to learn from Coyle.

Again, Scott snapped back to the moment. The squadron was coming up on their landing zone, a small airfield in the middle of the sea of green. Ba Tri airfield had limited space, but it was better than landing in a swamp. The pilots would land in shifts, deploy their troops, and take off again, circling above until the squadron was ready to return to Saigon for the next load of troops. It was going to be a long day.

When the helicopters landed the troops jumped out and took up defensive positions. It wasn't a hot landing zone, but nobody wanted to take any risks. They were in VC territory and the VC had proven to be sneaky little bastards. The area around the airfield was flat and covered with reeds which would mask the enemy's movements. The allied troops were trained to study the tops of the reeds to detect movement below. A gentle breeze made it more difficult because the reeds would move in unison like a series of waves. But the allies could still spot unusual movement of the reeds and fire a burst into the mass of reeds just to make sure. It would take a good part of the day to get the entire brigade plus the artillery on the ground.

It had been six months since ARVN forces had ventured into the Plain of Reeds. The Viet Cong had enjoyed the quiet and used the time to plan and resupply for their next campaign. They also reinforced their defenses by building beehive bunkers around their headquarters and along a nearby canal. The enemy's beehive bunkers were bell-shaped sandbag bunkers with firing ports built into the top. The enemy would stand inside the bunker and fire out one of the four gun ports when the allies approached. By standing in the bunker, the enemy had a much better view of the field of fire. There was only enough room for one or two soldiers with rifles. The sandbags could absorb all small arms fire and even heavy machine-gun bullets. A recoilless rifle or bazooka was needed to destroy the bunkers.

Once the artillery was in place and ready for fire missions, Williamson ordered the 1st Battalion, 503rd Infantry to be helelifted to a landing zone west of the Vam Co Dong River where they would carry out search-and-destroy operations. Lieutenant Colonel John Tyler was in command of 1/503.

A short time later, Williamson ordered the 1st Battalion, Royal Australian Regiment to be airlifted to an LZ east of the river to carry out search-and-destroy operations in the northeast sector. 2nd Battalion, 503rd Infantry would stay at the brigade's base at the airfield where they could quickly reinforce either of the two active battalions should they make heavy contact with the Viet Cong as hoped.

On the first day of the operation, each of the battalions in the field came into light contact with the enemy as their troops spread out in search of the VC. It wasn't what Williamson had expected. Intelligence reports had shown a large concentration of Viet Cong in the area. So far, it looked like the intelligence officers had missed the mark once again. The Viet Cong commanders might have recognized the superior force they were facing and had ordered their troops to bug out of the area.

Waiting at command headquarters at the airfield, Granier was aggravated. He could not deploy his students onto the battlefield until a significant firefight broke out and there were enemy targets available. He felt like he was wasting valuable time. While the would-be-snipers waited, Granier decided to instruct them on the terrain of the Mekong Delta and how to properly position themselves on the battlefield. It wasn't the same as an actual battle, but it was all he could offer them at the moment. He needed the shooting to start to train them properly in real-world conditions.

Later that day, Williamson decided to apply even more pressure in hopes of bringing the Viet Cong to battle. He wanted a fight and would do his darndest to get one. He ordered Tyler to once again helilift his battalion to another part of the area of operation – Landing Zone Vodka near Tra Cu.

Once again, the Americans encountered light resistance in their new area of operation. Several hours later, Tyler's battalion encountered an enemy force of about 60 VC armed with automatic weapons in bunkers near the river. B Company engaged the enemy pinning them down as artillery and air strikes pounded the VC positions.

Hearing the radio transmissions of the battle, Granier gathered his team of students, boarded Scott's helicopter, and took off in search of the battle. It didn't take long. He asked Scott to set down near the firefight but not so near they would come under fire. Granier did not want to lose any of his students unnecessarily.

When the helicopter landed and Granier and his students disembarked, they took up defensive positions just like a regular squad of infantry. When the helicopter took off, Granier signaled his students to follow him toward the firefight. They moved cautiously. As they approached the fighting, Granier pointed out possible fire positions for each of the teams, but he let them select their positions. Once everyone was set up, the gunfire ceased. The battle was over.

After an hour of brutal punishment from Tyler's company and artillery barrages, the Viet Cong had broken contact and retreated to the south.

Granier was furious and cussed like a sailor. He hated his job as an instructor, the shake-and-bake sniper program, and the stupid Marauder Operation that was turning into a big waste of time for everyone. He and his students climbed back into Scott's helicopter and returned to the airfield to wait for another opportunity… if there was one.

Williamson was angry that Tyler had let the enemy escape and didn't chase after them. Tyler explained that the Viet Cong had dispersed into squad-sized units and there was no main body to pursue. Besides, friendly artillery and airstrikes on the fleeing Viet Cong troops made it too dangerous to chase them.

The task force commander ordered the Australian battalion commander, Lieutenant Colonel Alex Preece to airlift his troops to the east side of the Vam Co Dong River near the village of Can Thuy. As they landed, the Australians found little opposition and lots of abandoned enemy bunkers. It seemed the Viet Cong had left in a hurry.

Even with the short battle involving Tyler's battalion, the gains of the task force were minimal, and Williamson was beyond frustrated. Enemy sniper fire was also a growing problem as the allied units advanced. All of the units involved in the Marauder Operation had encountered knee-deep water in rice paddies and sugar cane fields that had been flooded making mobility a problem. The chest-deep streams and canals that crisscrossed the area had thick layers of silt on the bottoms that could easily strand a soldier mid-stream and make him an easy target. The strike force was quickly losing its biggest advantage – mobility. The putrid stench of the mud was lowering morale and making some of the troops sick. If his forces could not engage the Viet Cong, Williamson knew that Operation Marauder would be a failure and failure was not an option the task force leader was willing to accept. The mission was clearly in trouble.

The next morning, Williamson ordered Lieutenant Colonel George Dexter, the commander of the 2nd Battalion, 503rd Infantry, to helilift some of his units to Landing Zone Wine in the southeast sector where they too would begin search-and-destroy operations. The 2/503 was the task force ready reserve, but without enemy contact, Williamson saw little need for such a large reserve. The battalion's C and D companies became the reserve and remained at headquarters along with 16th Armor.

Before flying his battalion into the landing zone, Dexter ordered airstrikes and artillery barrages to clear the area. Helicopter gunships laid down more fire just before the transport helicopters landed. Dexter wasn't taking any chances. Many thought he was being overly cautious since no heavy enemy contact had occurred with the other battalions. But as the air assault unfolded, Dexter's caution served him and his men well…

As the gunships swooped over the landing zone unleashing their rocks and strafing the area with their machine guns, they encountered dense groundfire from the enemy's heavy machine guns hidden in the reeds. The VC battalions traveled with their air defenses indicating that there was a large enemy force surrounding Landing Zone Wine.

Dexter ordered the transport helicopters to change course and land his battalion 500 yards northeast of the LZ Wine. It was a smart move. B Company was the first to land. The troops spread out quickly in a cane field forming their defensive positions parallel to the VC on LZ Wine. They were met with sporadic enemy fire and a few soldiers in the company were wounded. Two of the helicopters took fire and one of the door gunners was killed falling from the aircraft as it ascended into the sky. With his chest stitched with enemy bullets; he was dead before he hit the ground.

Hearing the radio reports, Williamson and his staff realized that the Viet Cong had been using the flooded rice paddies and fields to funnel the task force units into preset ambushes. The Plain of Reeds was a well-laid-out trap.

Granier also heard the reports on the radio and decided to fly his trainees to Landing Zone Wine. It was premature to call the skirmish an actual battle, but Granier had a feeling he wouldn't be disappointed. No matter what, he didn't want to miss another opportunity by arriving too late. They would go and hope that a battle would develop. It was a strange wish. If correct, soldiers were going to die. He and his men scrambled out to the helicopter flight line and jumped in their chopper. A few minutes later, Scott lifted off, banked hard, and headed for the Landing Zone. Granier's students were excited. This is what they had been trained to do. Now, they would test their skills and with any luck impress their teacher enough to let them pass the course to become full-fledged snipers.

Shortly after that, A Company landed, and its troops moved south in an attempt to link up with B Company's left flank. But before they could make contact with their sister company, both companies came under heavy fire and were pinned down by a large concentration of enemy bunkers 100 yards to the southwest. Unknowingly, the 2/503 had engaged the Viet Cong's entrenched 267th Main Force Battalion.

A VC machine gun inside a concrete bunker laid down a heavy fusillade on B Company inflicting multiple wounds in the platoon holding the left flank. B Company commander, Captain Les Brownlee ordered an airstrike to take out the enemy machine-gun emplacement. As an assault aircraft approached from the rear of the VC lines, a bomb hung up, then freed itself and dropped late onto the battlefield. The misplaced bomb exploded in B Company's lines killing four and wounding six troopers. In addition to the loss of manpower in the middle of a firefight, company morale was crushed. Brownlee did what he could to rally his soldiers as they fought for their lives.

Mired down in a marsh, A Company continued its efforts to link up with B Company's lines. A Company commander, Captain Carmen Cavezza called in artillery strikes but was told that the enemy and friendly lines were too close. The Viet Cong had grabbed their enemy by the belt and weren't about to let go. Cavezza ordered his company mortar teams to provide fire support, but they were unable to set up properly in the open paddies filled with mud and water. If they set up on the dry dikes that divided the fields, they would be exposed to heavy enemy fire. The captain could see that it was a lose-lose situation and rescinded his order commanding instead that the mortar teams grab their personal weapons and join the firing line.

An Air Force FAC piloting his Cessna O-1 Bird Dog flew low over the battlefield in hopes of better identifying the enemy positions and calling in an artillery strike. Unknowingly, the pilot flew over the strike force's artillery battery just as it fired a new barrage. A shell struck the aircraft blowing it to smithereens and instantly killing the Forward Air Controller.

Among the chaos, Granier and his students landed and poured out of the helicopter. They immediately took fire. Granier was pleased. This was a real battle and lives were on the line. That's what his trainees needed, a taste of reality. He belly-crawled off the landing zone and into a tall clump of elephant grass. His students followed. He instructed them to listen to the gunfire to determine the location of the friendly and enemy lines. AK-47s, the preferred weapon of the Viet Cong, had a distinct sound when fired. By listening, the trainees could determine where and how far the position of the enemy was located. They also listened to the sound of the American weapons and pinned their location. Knowing where both lines were allowed the snipers to determine where they needed to be to fire on the enemy. They searched for high ground. There was none except for the earthen dikes that separated the rice paddies. The elevation of the dikes was only three feet above the fields but that was enough to give the snipers an edge. Even if they were at the same height as the enemy that was better than shooting up.

The sniper teams spread out across the dikes surrounding two rice paddies near the enemy lines. Crawling up to the top of one of the dikes, Granier could see the enemy soldiers using a vertical dike for cover. The snipers were slightly behind the enemy. He couldn't ask for a much better position. He instructed the students to fire the first rounds in unison while their position was still unknown to the enemy. After that, they could fire when ready. Enemy commanders were the top target and NCOs were next in line. Decapitating the enemy units was the goal. Chaos would surely ensue among the enemy ranks if the snipers were successful.

Granier waited until all five teams were in position and had acquired their first targets before giving the command to fire in a low voice.

When the sniper shots cracked, five Viet Cong

commanders and NCOs dropped dead rolling down the embankment into the brown paddy water.

The sniper teams were exuberant patting each other on the back for their first kill. Granier snarled. This was not the time to celebrate. The sniper teams snapped around and acquired their next targets. It wasn't as easy this time. The Viet Cong had figured out that there was a fire team behind their position and were pouring fire on the sniper's positions. This was the reality of the battlefield, and their instructor loved it. Granier desperately wanted to join the fight, but he knew that wasn't his job at the moment. He watched sniper teams throwing small rocks at them when he had a suggestion. It was an ill-mannered but effective technique. One rarely forgot the instruction given after being pelted with a rock.

Over the battalion radio, Dexter requested that Williamson release his two companies held in reserve at headquarters along with 16th Armor. Williamson granted his request. Dexter ordered his infantry companies and the armor commanders to move their forces to the southwest of A Company and outflank the Viet Cong battalion. Everything went according to plan until the armored vehicles bogged down in the thick mud near Ap Tho, two miles from A Company's position. Slogging their way through the mud, the two infantry companies continued toward the battlefield without the armor. It was slow going. They did not reach the battlefield until late in the afternoon eight hours after the firefight had begun. The troops in the reinforcement companies were exhausted and badly in need of food and water before they could fight effectively. In the meantime, the Air Force and artillery batteries were doing what they could to keep the enemy from overrunning B and C Companies. Because of the closeness of the lines, their options were limited to assaulting enemy machine guns and mortar positions.

Once the two companies had rested for a few minutes, Dexter ordered all his men to attack the enemy lines from the southwest. A massive firefight ensued as both sides struggled to gain and keep territory. The situation changed radically when a platoon from A Company overran an enemy flank position next to a long line of concrete bunkers. Using grenades and satchel charges, the American forces were able to roll up the VC forces in their bunkers one at a time.

The VC commander of the 267th could see that his defensive line was crumbling as the Americans advanced. He ordered all his mortar teams to focus their fire on their flanks.

The Americans were forced to seek cover as mortar shells rained down, exploding, and sending tons of mud mixed with shrapnel into the air. Having fought for eight hours straight, the VC mortar teams were low on ammunition and the shelling soon tapered off allowing the Americans to resume their roll-up operation. The VC commander was out of options and didn't want to sacrifice his men for nothing. He ordered a general retreat. The VC fled west toward the river firing their weapons as they retreated.

Granier's students did their best to pick off the fleeing Viet Cong, but it was a mad rush with shots being fired in all directions. Granier ordered his men to keep their heads down. They had done enough damage and didn't need to die to prove their worth. Granier would pass all five teams after the battle.

As they climbed over the last dike, the Americans saw 98 VC bodies and six enemy wounded lying in the mud surrounded by their equipment. The Americans and their allies had won. It was Dexter's quick thinking to not deploy directly on Landing Zone Wine that had prevented his troops from being slaughtered by the VC ambush waiting for them. Had B Company been wiped out at the beginning of the battle, the results could have been much different.

In the days that followed the firefight on Landing Zone Wine, the Americans, Australians, and New Zealanders all uncovered large weapon and ammunition caches in the area of operations. The caches were boobytrapped and mined. Special teams of mine detection and demolition were brought in to clear each of the caches before any weapons or ammunition were removed. In addition, allied forces recovered hundreds of documents at the enemy command headquarters including a list of all the soldiers in each of the units within the VC battalions operating in the area. Operation Marauder continued until January 8th when it was terminated and replaced with Operation Crimp.

COURT AT THE CARAVELLE

Washington D.C., USA

Deep in thought, Karen Dickson stood at a counter in a gun shop. She was still struggling with her decision to bring a gun with her to Vietnam. The American photojournalist Dickey Chapelle had often carried a rifle with her when she was embedded with the U.S. military. She had been killed by a booby trap while out on patrol in the highlands a few months earlier. Karen admired her and was determined to continue her legacy.

Four pistols – a Walther PPK, a Colt Detective Special, a Colt M1911A, and a Smith & Wesson Model 10 - rested on a felt pad so as not to scratch the glass. A clerk patiently waited for her decision. She picked up each gun checking for weight, balance, and the fit of the grip as a friend that knew guns had suggested. Her stepfather, the Colonel, had taught her to shoot his Colt M1911. It was a cannon and the recoil threatened to wrestle the pistol from her hands. The weight was also a problem. She planned on carrying the gun everywhere she would go in Vietnam and weight mattered. The only advantage the pistol had was that the .45 caliber ammunition could stop a charging enemy soldier dead in his tracks. She set the M1911 aside. It was a possibility but not a probability.

Next, she picked up the Smith & Wesson Model 10, a revolver. It was lighter than the M1911 and the grip was slightly curved making it easier to hold. It was also a revolver and less prone to jamming which made it more reliable than the semi-automatics. She didn't like the long barrel which threw off the balance and made it more difficult to draw from a holster. It used .38 caliber ammunition which was also less powerful than the .45. She set it aside.

The Walther PPK was next. She picked it up. It felt good in her hand. "That's James Bond's weapon," said the clerk as if that were an important factor. "It fires a .32 caliber bullet. You can buy ammunition just about anywhere in the world. Not too much recoil. Good weapon for a lady."

Karen liked the availability of ammunition and the limited recoil features. It was also smaller than the other two pistols. But James Bond or not, it was an automatic and that meant it could jam at an inopportune time. What was the point of carrying a gun if you couldn't use it when you needed it most?

She set the Walther PPK down and moved on to the Colt Detective Special, a revolver. It had a shorter barrel than the Colt Model 10 but still fired a .38 caliber bullet. It was also a double-action revolver meaning that it could be fired by simply pulling the trigger and didn't require the gun's hammer to be pulled back. It felt heavier than the Walther but not enough to discourage her. Its frame was small making it easy to hold. She thought for a moment, then said, "I'll take this one."

"Good choice. It's been around for a long time. Very reliable. Do you need ammunition or a holster?" said the clerk.

"Yes. Both. And a cleaning kit."

"How many boxes of ammunition?"

"How many shells are in a box?"

"Fifty."

"Three boxes then. Is there a gun range nearby?"

"There's an indoor range on 12th and Harbor. The owner knows his guns. He can help you if you have any questions. What kind of holster do you want? Waistband or shoulder?"

"What do you recommend?"

"Well, if you are going to be walking a lot the waistband holster can irritate your hip bone."

"I am going to be walking a lot. Let me have a shoulder holster."

"Okay. If you don't mind me asking… Where are you headed?"

"Vietnam."

"Are you a nurse?"

"No. Photojournalist."

"I didn't know the military allowed female photographers in a war zone."

"Yeah. They do."

"Kinda dangerous, don't ya think?"

"I imagine."

"Best keep your head down."

"Good thinking. I'll do that," she said with a bit of cynicism in her voice.

Karen had been patronized by men her entire life. She knew better than to argue with the clerk. People don't change and she was not responsible for the clerk's attitude toward women. Besides, the times were changing, and he would eventually catch up like most men.

Karen stood in an indoor shooting range stall. The range master had already clipped a paper target to the wire and sent it down range. He stood back and watched as she carefully loaded her new pistol. The Colt snub-nose had a Royal Blue finish and a walnut grip. It was a handsome piece of machinery. The revolver's cylinder held six shells. She closed it and looked for the safety. "Where's the safety?" she said.

"Revolvers don't have a safety," said the range master.

"Good to know. So, I just point and shoot?"

"Yep. Preferably down range."

Karen smiled at the man's wry sense of humor. She adjusted her shooting stance as the Colonel had taught her and took aim. She took a breath and let half of it out before slowly squeezing the trigger. A loud crack was accompanied by the gun's recoil.

Not bad, she thought. There was a hole on the left side of the target about three inches from the center. She aimed again and fired five rounds until the gun was empty. She set the gun down and reeled the target back to the stall. All six holes were on the left-middle of the target. "Nice grouping," said the range master looking over her shoulder.

"For a girl?" said Karen.

"For anyone. Who taught you to shoot?"

"My father. I mean... my stepfather. He was a military officer."

"He was a good teacher."

"Yeah, he was. Can you help me adjust the sight?"

"No. You have to reset the barrel and I don't have the proper tools. If it really bothers you, you should send it back to Colt and have them adjust it."

"I don't have the time. My flight's tomorrow."

"Then live with it. It's not off by much and you can adjust your aim to compensate."

"Alright."

She reloaded her weapon, clipped a new target to the wire, and sent it down range. She adjusted her aim as the range master had suggested and squeezed off another six rounds. When the paper target came back, there were six holes in the center with two in the bullseye. "That's a keeper," said the range master.

"Now if I can just remember to adjust my aim when under fire."

"Do you plan on getting shot at a lot? Are you a bank robber?"

Karen laughed.

Karen sat in Janet Dickerson's kitchen where they always ate because her mother didn't want to wash the tablecloth on the dining room table. Her mother had cooked one of Karen's favorite dishes, Cornish game hens stuffed with wild rice and gravy. Karen wondered if there were Cornish game hens in Vietnam... or maybe they ate pigeons instead. The thought made her shudder with disgust. They both sat silently eating which was odd. Her mother usually asked a lot of questions about what she was doing at work and if she was dating. But this time... silence. "Is there something wrong, Mom?" said Karen.

"No. I was just wondering when your flight takes off," said Janet.

"My flight?"

"Your brother ratted you out."

"Damn him. I should never have written him."

"You mean like you should have kept the truth from him like you kept it from me?"

"I wanted to tell you, but I didn't want you to worry."

"And not telling me makes it safer to work in a war zone?"

"No. It's just… complicated. I knew you'd try to talk me out of it."

"You're damned right I'm gonna try to talk you out of it. This is insane. Photographing riots and protests wasn't enough excitement?"

"That's not it, Mom. Somebody needs to tell this story… about the war."

"And that someone has to be my only daughter?"

"Yes. Because I want it. It's important."

"It's bad enough I need to worry about your brother being over there, risking his life. Now you?"

"Don't put that on me. That was Scott's decision. I didn't tell him to do it."

"So, answer my question… when?"

"Tomorrow night."

"Jesus. You weren't going to tell me."

"I was going to wait until I got over there, and you could see that I was being safe."

"And are you going to be safe?"

"Most of the time, yes."

"And the other times?"

"I'm a photojournalist, Mom. I need to go where the story takes me."

"You mean into the jungle?"

"Well, yeah… sometimes."

"And what if you're captured or wounded? You're

an American woman in a foreign country. Do you really think the Viet Cong are going to treat you with respect?"

"Probably not. So, I won't get captured or wounded."

"That's not up to you, is it?"

"Not all the time, but I'm a smart woman, Mom. I can take care of myself."

"I can't believe you are doing this to me."

"I'm not doing anything to you. This is my job. Vietnam is where the most important story of my generation is happening, and I need to be there to record it. I'm not going to die, Mom. I'm going to live. Maybe for the first time in my life."

"You're talking nonsense, Karen. You already live more than anyone I know."

Karen rose and said, "I've got to go. I still have a lot of things I need to do before my flight."

"Karen, wait…"

"No. It's better I go. We're both pigheaded and one of us might say something we might regret."

"I love you."

Her mother rarely said those words, not wanting to waste them on trivial moments. Karen stopped, turned, and said, "I love you too, Mom."

"Promise me you'll come back."

"You know I can't say that."

"Do it anyway. I need it."

"Okay. I promise."

The two women embraced and then Karen was gone. Three days later she was in Saigon.

Saigon, South Vietnam

Stepping off the Boeing 707 airliner, Karen thought she was prepared for Vietnam's weather. She wasn't. The wave of heat and humidity hit her like an open oven. Halfway down the stairs, she wanted to return to the comfort of the air-conditioned aircraft. It was too late. Saigon was calling her. There was no turning back.

She was already wearing her khaki jumpsuit. Her chosen attire for the jungles of Vietnam. Dickey Chapelle had worn a similar jumpsuit during her time in-country and Karen was sticking to Dickey's modus operandi whenever possible. Karen was quite a bit taller and filled out the jumpsuit better than Dickey who was a tiny, but fiery woman. With the top two buttons undone, Karen's tight jumpsuit looked somewhat sexy. That wasn't Karen's intent. She just wanted to keep cool. Her chest often glistened from sweat and caught the eye of many male passersby.

Once she gathered her luggage, an overstuffed rucksack she had purchased from an Army surplus store, she moved out into the main terminal and found her Vietnamese driver holding a hand-drawn sign with her name misspelled. Aside from his spelling, his English was understandable, and Karen began bombarding him with questions. He did his best to answer her questions and when he didn't know the answer, he would guess and act as if the answer was correct. That was the Vietnamese way – a guess was better than not knowing.

It was late in the afternoon and traffic was bumper to bumper mixed with motor scooters and tricycle taxis. Karen was anxious to reach her office and meet her bureau chief, Malcolm Browne. Browne was a legend in the community of war correspondents. He had won the World Press Photo of the Year for his iconic photo of the self-immolation of Buddhist monk Thich Quang Duc in Saigon in 1963. The next year, Browne won a Pulitzer Prize for his in-depth reporting on the Vietnam War. Karen could hardly believe she was working for such a man.

The sooner she could pick up an assignment the better. Before actually going into the field, she would need to visit the U.S. Embassy and apply for her press credentials. Once she had her credentials, she could embed with a U.S. military unit and go out on patrol or even a search & destroy operation. That was where the real action was... search & destroy operations. It seemed morbid to hope to cover such a mission but that was the job and Karen's deep desire was to bring her photos of the war to the world. The viewers could make up their own minds as to what was morbid and what was not.

Karen had originally planned on staying freelance while in Vietnam. She had grown accustomed to shooting what she wanted, when she wanted, and not having to meet the demands of an editor with deadlines. But after doing her research, she realized she would have her hands full of paperwork if she remained on her own. She also knew that her fellow journalists at a news organization could be a big help with introductions. Vietnam was new territory for Karen. It would take time to learn the ropes and make contacts, especially within the U.S. military.

Before leaving the states, she had applied for an overseas photojournalist position at the Associated Press (AP) in New York. She was surprised at how fast she got an interview. The editor was a fan of her work. He immediately offered her a job as a photojournalist in South Vietnam before someone else snapped her up.

It was just past 4 PM when they finally arrived at AP headquarters in downtown Saigon. She grabbed her bags and headed upstairs. To her surprise, the office was almost empty. She approached one of the two journalists left in the office and said, "Where is everyone?"

One of the journalists glanced at his watch and said, "Most likely they're all at the Caravelle."

"What the hell is the Caravelle?"

"It's a hotel where foreign journalists hang out and swap war stories. It's Happy Hour. Two for one."

The other journalist piped in, "Just say 'Caravelle' to your driver. He'll know where to go."

Karen was a bit surprised that almost everyone had left work so early in the afternoon. She picked up her bag and head back down the stairs.

When she reached the street, she saw that her chauffeur was already gone. She flagged a taxi, then motioned for the driver to roll down his window, and said, "Caravelle?"

He nodded like he knew where it was. She jumped in the back and he took off merging back into traffic. It suddenly occurred to Karan that she had not exchanged any of her money and had nothing to pay the driver. She held up a couple of dollar bills and said, "U.S. dollar, okay?"

The excited driver nodded and gave her a thumbs up as he said, "Dollar okie dokie."

She smiled, sat back, and relaxed. She didn't know what to expect, but she was sure she'd find a way to survive and maybe even thrive in Saigon. Vietnam was the adventure she had been hoping to find.

A half-hour later, the driver pulled up in front of the Caravelle Saigon. She paid the driver two dollars which seemed to more than satisfy him, grabbed her rucksack, and headed into the lobby. Unlike the famous Continental Hotel across the street, the Caravelle was a massive ten-story building. The lobby featured a marble floor, finely crafted modern furniture, and enormous bouquets of freshly cut flowers. The lounge was packed to the rafters and loud as hell with journalists laughing and shouting for friends to join them. Looking a bit downtrodden, Karen walked in with her rucksack. "Now there is a lost sheep if I have ever seen one," said a journalist with a cocktail in hand. "Who do you work for?"

"AP," she said.

"Malcolm's holding court in a booth in the back. Ya can't miss 'em. He's got his Pulitzer hung around his neck like an Olympic medal."

"Thanks," said Karen laughing as she pushed her way through the crowd knocking a few elbows and spilling drinks. It was happy hour. Nobody cared.

She found the AP crew in the corner. A group surrounded Peter Arnett a New Zealand-born American journalist that would win his own Pulitzer Prize later that year. Arnett didn't pull any punches when he reported, and his stories often had a negative slant on the war.

Another group surrounded Nick Ut, a Vietnamese-American photographer. Ut would go on to win both the Pulitzer Prize and World Press Photo of the Year for his photograph of a naked nine-year-old girl, Phan Thị Kim Phuc, running from a South Vietnamese napalm strike that mistakenly hit Trang Bang village.

Malcolm Browne was sitting in the middle of a corner booth drinking a cocktail. Karen was a little disappointed not to see his Pulitzer as advertised. Journalists were such liars, she thought. Someone grabbed Browne's attention and pointed to Karen and her rucksack. "You must be Karen Dickson?" said Browne.

"That's me," said Karen. "You must be Malcolm Browne."

"Yep. Last time I looked. I like your photographs. Good tension."

Karen laughed, "I like yours."

"Yeah, well… I got lucky. Let me buy you a drink. Actually, let me buy you two drinks."

"Thanks. I haven't exchanged any money yet."

"Ask Suni. She knows where to find the best rates," said Browne pointing to a woman in the next booth.

"Will do. When can I have my first assignment?"

Browne laughed, "Oh, to be young again."

"I'm serious."

"I know you are. That's what makes it so damned charming. I'll have something for you tomorrow after you pick up your press credentials at the embassy."

"Is that hard… getting press credentials?"

"No. This is the Vietnam War, not World War II. The American government doesn't give a damn anymore. You can say and shoot whatever you want as long as you don't give away a unit's position or disclose any operational plans."

"That's good, right?"

"Very good. But remember… to send your photos out over the wire, you have to run them by the South Vietnamese censors."

"Are they tough?"

"Not if you have the appropriate bribe."

"So, that's okay… bribing them?"

"No. It's damned rotten, but it's the cost of doing business in Saigon. I don't encourage it, but I won't forbid it either. What do you want to drink?"

"Do they have white wine?"

"Don't be a wimp, Dickson. You're a foreign photojournalist. Act like one."

"A whiskey sour then."

"Atta girl! Just remember… the key to survival is eating a big dinner after Happy Hour. Waiter, two whiskey sours!" bellowed Browne.

Karen knew she was gonna like it at AP. It would take time and a lot of whiskey sours to make friends, but they were her kinda people - rude, crude, and socially unacceptable. In many respects, they were the opposite of the anti-war protestors she had been photographing in the states. Those people were idealists fighting for a cause they believed in. The journalists in Vietnam seemed more practical and unafraid to bend the rules when required to get the story or the photograph. Of course, they all had their opinions about the war, but they didn't seem to be taking sides. All points of view were welcomed, even expected. When working with a bunch of veteran journalists, everyone knew that they had thought out their positions and therefore deserved respect even if they were wrong. Their job was to expose the truth and let the chips fall wherever they may. The overall mantra was "Let the reader decide."

KEYMAN

Saigon, South Vietnam

Karen was hungover when she received her press credentials from the MACV Press office in the embassy. When handed the card in a plastic cover, she asked, "When can I embed with a military unit?"

"That's up to the individual unit commander, but I'll warn you… it's a long line. There are over three hundred foreign journalists in South Vietnam, and they all want the same thing just like you."

"So, how do I jump to the head of the line?"

The officer laughed, "You don't. But a bottle of good scotch wouldn't hurt."

"Thanks. Where can I get good scotch?"

"Get out of my office."

Karen left. Walking down the staircase she noticed a soldier double-timing the stairs on his way up. He was wearing a camouflaged uniform without insignia and had the deep tan of a man that had spent a lot of time in the field. His rolled-up shirt sleeves revealed his muscular forearms and his neck looked like a tree stump. He was older and not overly good-looking, but Karen found him attractive. The man was oblivious like he had something more important on his mind than a young woman's ogling. As they passed each other on the stairs, Karen didn't realize that the man knew her father, Tom Coyle, and her brother Scott Dickson. She took a second glance before Rene Granier disappeared through a doorway. "Come to Mama," she said quietly to herself as she continued down the stairs. Even though he was old enough to be her father, Granier was the kinda trouble Karen liked.

Granier had been called into MACV when he returned from the Plain of Reeds. He surmised that the officer in charge of the program wanted a report on the results of the first shake-and-bake sniper school. He brought his evaluation of his trainees with him. The officers at MACV loved data that they could pass on to Secretary of Defense Robert McNamara, a true data wonk. Granier told the receptionist he was there to see the Lt. Colonel in charge of the program and sat down in the waiting area. It didn't take long before he was ushered into the office.

Moving into the office, he saw another man with his back to him already sitting across from the light colonel. The colonel greeted Granier, then excused himself, and left the office closing the door behind him. The man in the seat turned around and said, "Have a seat, Granier."

He was the shadowy figure Granier knew as "Bill" that carried covert orders from the director of the CIA. "What are you doing here, Bill?" said Granier still standing by the door.

"Sit down and you'll find out."

Granier sat reluctantly. Bill was not the kinda guy that brought good news. He was the kinda guy that got things done by any means necessary. Covert things. Dangerous things. Bill handed him an envelope. Granier opened it and read. It was another letter from the Director of the CIA instructing Officer Rene Granier to follow the instructions given by the man delivering the letter he held. "Okay. What now?"

"It's good to see you too," said Bill.

"I didn't say that."

"I know, but you meant it in your heart."

"Enough of the pleasantries. What do you want?"

"The director would like you to take charge of a new pilot program called, 'Operation Keyman."

"Okay. What is it?"

"When the man you previously assassinated was discovered, the director realized the extensive damage such a man could bring against the South Vietnamese and U.S. military effort. Nobody knows how many secrets Colonel Thao revealed to the Northern Intelligence service and Viet Cong. The director believes he may have been a big part of the South Vietnamese Military's difficulties in the last few years."

"He's dead. Problem solved."

"Not really."

"How's that?"

"There are others like Thao. And they may not all be in the military. The director believes there are 'keymen' sent to infiltrate the South. Some may be sleeper agents not yet activated. Others may be agitators in the countryside or smaller cities."

"And the director wants them eliminated?"

"Eventually, yes. But first, we need to discover the secrets they have revealed and who their associates might be."

"I don't torture people if that's what you're asking."

"We don't expect you to. We will assemble a team of experts in the required fields of operation. You can help choose them."

"I'm not interested. You've got the wrong guy."

"Granier, why did you originally join the military?"

"To serve and protect my country."

"This program could win the war if implemented correctly."

"I think that's a stretch, but I get your point."

"If we can cut off the flow of intelligence to the North, is there any doubt our soldiers in the field would be safer?"

"You're talking about torture. I can't do that."

"How is it any different from what you're doing now?"

"I don't torture prisoners."

"We can make sure you have arm's length from those activities."

"I'd be part of it even if I didn't hold the pliers directly."

"Yes, you would. But you'd also be saving hundreds, maybe even thousands of American lives. You and your team could turn the tide of battles."

"I'm not saying these types of programs are not useful. I'm just saying I don't want to be a part of them."

"So, basically you're willing to pass the responsibility on to someone else's shoulders?"

"I do my part. That should be enough."

"And we are grateful for your efforts. That's why you're here. If we are going to win this war, we need you and your team to do what the U.S. Military cannot.

The one thing I can guarantee you is that the communists have similar programs, and they are effective. We haven't had a successful agent insertion in the North in months. They've cut off our intelligence efforts. We need to do the same to level the playing field. If this program is successful, we can expand it countrywide and that could make a huge difference in the war."

Granier didn't respond. Bill could see that he had pushed the man enough and said, handing Granier another package with a book inside, "You should read this before making up your final decision."

"Alright," said Granier glancing at the book and its author – French General Paul Aussaresses.

Bill wrote down a phone number on a slip of paper, handed it to Granier, and said, "I'll be in Saigon for another three days. Think about what I said. If you change your mind, call me. We need you, Granier."

Granier slipped the phone number into his shirt pocket. Bill rose and walked out leaving Granier with his thoughts. Granier was not squeamish about killing the enemy. He had come to grips with that years ago. But the idea of torturing another human turned his stomach. He didn't want to become someone that could do that on a daily basis and still sleep at night. Although few and far between, he still had morals and lines he wouldn't cross. This was one of them. His mind made up, he rose, and walked out. But Bill's words "…you're willing to pass the responsibility on to someone else's shoulders?" bothered him. He was not one to shirk responsibility and he knew deep down that he was the right guy for this program even if it didn't fit well with his morals. The longer the war went on, the more American soldiers would die. Even if he could shorten the war by a few months, it would mean thousands of American and South Vietnamese lives saved. And if he didn't accept the assignment, their deaths were on him. It was a shitty thing Bill was asking him to do but was it the right thing? The thing that could truly make a difference.

Having received a telegram from Janet Dickson, Karen and Scott's mother, Coyle had flown to Saigon. Janet's telegram had instructed Coyle to protect Karen as if he had some magical power to do so. It was similar to the conversation they had about their son, Scott when Coyle first found out that he had two children with Janet that he never knew about. Janet was a force to be reckoned with, especially when it came to her children. It was easier to just do what she said rather than argue the point. Coyle would do the best he could. He was a little hurt that his daughter hadn't bothered to inform him that she was coming to Vietnam, but he recognized that she probably didn't want another lecture on the dangers that Coyle was sure her mother had given her. He didn't want the first meeting with his newfound daughter to end in an argument. He decided to be calm and listen for a change.

Coyle took a taxi to the Caravelle Saigon where Karen was staying until she could find more permanent quarters, or better yet until she was embedded with the U.S. Military. Coyle knew that the foreign journalists hung out at the Caravelle, and he suspected that Karen, being a newbie, wouldn't want her father showing up unannounced.

When he arrived, he stepped into the lobby, picked up a house phone, and asked for Karen Dickson. As the phone rang, Coyle started sweating. He was nervous as hell. Someone picked up the other end and said, "Hello?"

"Karen?" said Coyle, his voice cracking a bit.

"Yes."

"This is Tom Coyle. I'm in the lobby. I was wondering if I could take you to dinner."

There was a long pause before Karen continued, "My mother sent you, didn't she?"

Coyle took a moment to consider his answer and decided on the truth, "Yes. But I would have come anyway if I had known you were here."

"You're wasting your time if you think you can convince me to go back to the states."

"No. I just really want to meet you. I promise I won't try to convince you of anything. You're a grown woman. It's your life. I understand that."

"Where do you want to have dinner? I don't have a lot of time."

"How about here in the hotel dining room? That's easy and I've heard it's pretty good."

"Alright. I need a few minutes."

"Take all the time you need. I'll get us a table. I'll see when you get there."

She hung up. Coyle smiled to himself. He was about to meet his daughter.

The waiter served their meals. Coyle had ordered a medium rare steak and Karen had ordered a bowl of Pho. "I guess that's new to you... Vietnamese food," said Coyle.

"Yeah. It's pretty good. Although I don't know what's in it."

"Better not to ask. Just know it probably won't kill you. Forty million Vietnamese can't be wrong."

Karen dipped her spoon in the broth and a chicken's foot rose to the top. "Oh, Jesus," said Karen.

"They're a delicacy. The toenails are especially good. Crunchy."

"I don't know if I can eat this."

"Do you like steak?"

"Yeah, if it's not overcooked."

Coyle lifted the bowl of pho and replaced it with his steak. "You don't have to do that," said Karen.

"It's fine. I like pho."

"Thanks," said Karen as she dug into the steak. "This is good."

Coyle smiled a little. He liked making her happy. "So, any idea where you'll be assigned?"

"Not really. I'm waiting to get embedded with a U.S. unit. There's a long line of more experienced photojournalists in front of me."

"So, what do you do in the meantime?"

"Hang around Saigon and try to make an impression."

"If you want, I could make some calls and see if I can get you moved up the list?"

"You can do that?"

"Sure. I've paid my dues. It's time I got something back."

"That would be a big help. I want to go where the action is, maybe the Central Highlands or the Mekong Delta."

"Okay. I'll see what I can do."

Coyle was lying and he felt a little guilty. But there was no way he was going to put his daughter in harm's way. He would find the most boring post in South Vietnam and make sure Karen was assigned to it. "Have you seen Scott lately?" said Karen with a mouth full of steak.

"Last week. We try to have lunch or dinner together whenever both of us are at the base."

"He ratted me out to Mom, the bastard."

Coyle was shocked to hear his son being called a "bastard" and wanted to come to his defense but decided it was better to keep his mouth shut. Besides, Coyle knew that Scott could fight his own battles. "You, two are close?" said Coyle.

"I suppose. But he can be a little overprotective at times."

"I see. And you don't like that?"

"Of course not. So, you fly for the CIA?"

Coyle looked around for anyone that might have heard her. "Yes, but we don't really talk about that."

"Oh, sorry."

"It's alright. We call it 'The Company.'"

"Okay. So, any chance I could fly with you on a mission?"

"No. But if you want, I can borrow a small plane and show you around the area."

"That's not as interesting as getting shot at."

"No, but it's a hell of a lot safer."

"There you are being overprotective."

"You're right. I am. But I'm still not taking you with me."

"Okay. I'll ask Scott to take me."

"Things can get pretty hairy on his missions."

"I hope so. Girl's got to make a living."

Karen noticed Coyle fidgeting and said, "I'll be okay, Coyle. Like you said, 'I'm a grown woman.'"

"Sorry. I guess I wasn't prepared for how grown."

"That's a good thing, right? You missed the teenage years."

Her comment stung Coyle and he said, "I would like to have seen you as a teenager, Scott too."

"We were both a handful."

"I imagine. Still, I'm sad I wasn't there."

"Wasn't your fault. Our's neither. We didn't even know you existed. We can all blame Mom for that one."

"Do you do that a lot… blame Mom?"

"Watch out, Coyle. You don't want to get between a mother and her daughter. It's dangerous territory."

"I'll remember that. Do you want another whiskey sour?"

"Better not. I've got a meeting with my boss in a few minutes. It would be good if I was sober."

Coyle laughed. It wasn't the easiest conversation he ever had, but he sure liked her spunk.

When Coyle returned to the CIA officer's quarters that the officers used when he Saigon, he was surprised to find Granier there, sitting on the back patio reading a book. He walked out and greeted Granier, "What are you doing here?" said Granier.

"I just met my daughter for the first time," said Coyle.

"Wow. Is she what you expected?"

"Far more."

"I suppose that's good."

"Very good."

"What's she doing here?"

"Photojournalist for the Associated Press. What are you reading?"

"Homework."

Coyle looked at the title and the author and said, "Paul Aussaresses? Why are you reading that crap?"

"Like I said… homework. Do you know him?"

"I've met him once. That was enough."

"Algeria?"

"Yeah, during the war for independence."

"Little Bruno was there?"

"Yeah. He became one of Aussaresses's disciples. He thought torturing rebels was the fastest way to win the war."

"And did it work?"

"Yeah, it did, but not until a lot of people suffered a great deal."

"I see. You know, I think about what we do and how we should do it. I wonder if mercy lengthens the war and ends up costing more lives in the long run?"

"I'm sure it does, but it also keeps us human. Animals rarely show mercy. So, why are you really reading his book?"

"Job offer."

"Believe me when I say, you don't want to become like Aussaresses. He's a bloodthirsty savage with no conscience. Turn it down, Granier."

"I already have, but for some reason, it's not sitting right with me. I can't sleep."

"Take pills then, but don't buy into Aussaresses's lies. Life's too short."

"Yeah, but… what if he's right. What if his methods really can shorten the war?"

"I don't know, but I saw a lot of inhumanity in Algeria. I don't want to live in a world that accepts that kind of behavior. We built the Hague to stop that sort of thing from ever happening again."

"Yeah. I hear you."

"Well, I am a little drunk from whiskey sours. I think I'll hit the rack."

"Good plan."

"I'll see you in the morning."

Coyle moved off to find a bunk. Granier continued reading and thinking. Coyle wasn't wrong but that didn't mean he was right either. Coyle's opinions didn't make Granier's decision any easier. He liked Coyle but considered him a bit of a pansy at times. War was a hard thing and it needed hard men like himself if America was going to win.

Later that night, Granier finished his book and sat thinking for a long while. What should have been an easy decision, wasn't. He was a patriot and wanted to do whatever was required for America to win the Vietnam War and stop communist expansion. He had been tortured by the Japanese after being captured during World War II. He felt real compassion for those that suffered from intense interrogation. That made him wonder if he was really the right man for the job. But one thing he knew for sure was that if he took the job of putting together the Keyman Program, he would do it all the way and not shirk off the parts he found distasteful. The real question was… would the program end the war sooner or was that just another Langley pipe dream? He knew that there was really only one way to find out.

After a few more minutes of sitting in silence and staring into the darkness, he rose and walked to the phone. He pulled out the piece of paper Bill had given him and dialed. When Bill answered, Granier simply said, "It's Granier. I'm in," and hung up.

January 12, 1966 - Washington D.C., USA

As was the tradition, President Johnson stood before a joint session of congress and delivered his State of the Union address. As was expected, the Democrats clapped louder than the Republicans, but everyone was well-behaved and acted like they were interested in what Johnson had to say. It was a time of manners and decorum. It wasn't that senators and congressmen didn't object to Johnson's proposals, they just waited until the appropriate time to stab the president in the back with their biting comments and critical jabs.

Johnson had just announced a huge budget of $110 billion to fund the Vietnam War and his social program called "The Great Society." While Johnson's social program met with strong headwinds from the Republicans, the war still had broad support in government and the audience clapped loudly whenever the war was mentioned.

OPERATION VAN BUREN

January 15, 1966 - Tuy Hoa Valley, Phu Yen
Province, South Vietnam

The rice in the paddy fields had turned golden brown as the harvest began. It was back-breaking work but also a time of celebration. The results of the harvest would determine how villages would fair that year.

The villagers wore conical hats made of straw to shade their heads as they lined up at the edge of the fields and used sharpened sickles to cut the rice plants at their base. Once started, they would not stop until the entire field was harvested. Few farmers had machines. Most of the work was done by hand. Bundles of rice stalks were carried out of the fields by wooden shoulder yokes or in handwoven baskets. Only small children and the very old were exempt from work during the harvest. Everyone else pitched in and did their part according to their ability. With little money in the community, extra helpers were paid in bags of rice at the end of the harvest.

Rice was a major target for the combatants whose strategy depended on who controlled the territory at the time of harvest. The Americans often fought to prevent the Viet Cong from stealing the farmers' rice or setting the fields and villages ablaze if the farmers were found to support the Viet Cong.

While the Viet Cong encouraged those farmers that paid their taxes to the communist shadow government and prevented farmers who refused to pay taxes from harvesting their crops under threat of death. The Viet Cong needed the rice to feed their troops the following year and would often wait until a traitorous farmer was finished with his harvest before stealing his entire crop as a punishment for not paying his taxes.

Caught in between, most farmers cared little about politics and often paid taxes to both sides so they could harvest their crops in peace and live another year to support their families.

Sparsely populated, Phu Yen was part of South Vietnam's South-Central Coast and with year-round access to water from the rivers a major rice-growing region. Most of the farmers that lived along the lower Da Rang River were ethnic Kinh. There were also minorities of Cham, E De, and Ba Na people living in outlying districts.

Operation Van Buren was a rice harvest security mission carried out by the U.S. 1st Brigade, 101st Airborne Division. In 1965, much of the valley's harvest had been requisitioned by NVA and Viet Cong forces to feed their troops. MACV didn't want to see the enemy confiscation repeated and sent 101st to stop them.

The NVA 95th Regiment, 5th Division was positioned in the mountains around the Tuy Hoa Valley and hoping the Americans would attack. Before the harvest began, the NVA and Viet Cong set up fortified blocking positions to ambush the Americans should they try to sweep the area. The VC were ready and anxious to fight and so were the NVA.

U.S. 2nd Battalion, 502nd Infantry Regiment, 101st Airborne Division arrived at the Tuy Hoa Airfield and deployed into defensive positions. Three days later transported by LST, 2nd Battalion, 327th Infantry Regiment landed at Tuy Hoa Port. The 2/502nd patrolled north of the Da Rang River while the 2/237th and the South Korean 2nd Marine Brigade patrolled to the south of the river.

Little resistance was met, until January 31st when the South Korean Marines walked into an NVA ambush and suffered heavy losses. The Koreans withdrew and were replaced by the U.S. 1/327th.

Six days later as it approached the hamlet of Canh Tanh 4, a platoon from Company B, 2/502nd, came under heavy fire. The company commander sent platoons to the south and the west of Canh Tanh 4 in hopes of encircling the enemy troops. Once in position, the American platoons attacked and were met with heavy enemy fire. None of the platoons could maneuver to support the others. Instead of slugging it out with enemy troops, all three American platoons withdrew. That allowed American aircraft an open battlefield which the pilots took great advantage of by thrashing the enemy with thirteen airstrikes, one right after the other. The U.S. forces on the ground tightened their defensive positions and prepared to resume their assault on the hamlet in the morning.

When the Americans rose the next morning and maneuvered to assault the hamlet, they found it empty. The enemy had withdrawn leaving the bodies of thirty-nine of their comrades.

That same day, Company C 2/502nd approached the

My Canh 2 hamlet just a mile and a half from Canh Tanh 4 when they too came under heavy fire from enemy forces entrenched around the hamlet. The American company was pinned down and taking losses. American air and artillery strikes pounded the enemy positions keeping the enemy from overrunning the American company. Reinforcements were requested by the company commander. Flown in by helicopters, Company B and Tiger Force of the 1st Battalion, 327th Regiment, commanded by Major David Hackworth, landed nearby. Hackworth saw the pinned-down company as an opportunity to kill the enemy who had been pinned down by the air and artillery strikes. Hackworth sent Tiger Force to the north of the hamlet and Company B to the south. The idea was to execute a hammer and anvil attack on the enemy force.

As Tiger Force moved into position the unit commander noticed that the cover was thinning out leaving his men in the open. Moments later, the entire Tiger Force was hit by a heavy barrage of enemy gunfire, and seven Americans were killed. Seeing Tiger Force pinned down and taking heavy casualties, Hackworth ordered Company B to attack in hopes of taking some of the pressure off Tiger Force. It didn't work. As they approached Tiger Force's position, Company B also was caught in the open with proper cover and came under heavy attack from an enemy ambush and lost nineteen soldiers in the first minutes of battle. The Americans were in a terrible position with all their units pinned down and taking heavy fire. They fought as best they could.

As night fell, Hackworth was able to consolidate Company B and Tiger Force into a defensive perimeter. Under the cover of darkness, the enemy moved their machine gun emplacements closer to the American lines. The enemy waited for the Americans to attack once more. When B Company and Tiger Force rose and attacked in the darkness, the enemy opened fire once again driving the Americans back. It was Tiger Forces unit commander Lieutenant James Gardner that tipped the battle in the Americans' favor when he single-handedly destroyed four enemy machine gun positions using hand grenades. Freeing up Tiger Force and B Company to advance, Gardner was struck down by an enemy bullet and killed. Gardner would be posthumously given the Medal of Honor for his bravery in combat.

The following morning, after a tense night of skirmishes, the American forces left their defensive positions and entered My Canh 2. The enemy was gone. The only thing that remained with the bodies of sixty-three communists that had been abandoned in the night.

Operation Van Buren continued without any major engagements with the enemy. The NVA and the Viet Cong had retreated from the area leaving the farmers to harvest their rice in peace. Surprisingly, even though the Americans had been ambushed multiple times during the operation, it was the NVA and Viet Cong that suffered the greatest number of casualties at 346 killed and thirty-three captured. The Americans had lost fifty-five, while the South Koreans had forty-five killed. The operational commander, Brigadier General Willard Pearson declared Operation Van Buren a success and MACV agreed with him.

Kien Tuong Province, South Vietnam

In the late afternoon, a bus filled with shoppers returning from market sped along the highway. Families shared the food they had purchased for the ride back to their villages. Most of the children were sleeping oblivious to the loud engine and chatting.

As the bus passed a clump of trees, a Viet Cong sapper used a mechanical plunge detonator to set off the mine he had placed in a pothole in the highway's asphalt. The mine exploded underneath the bus launching the front wheels into the air and tearing the bus in two. When the remains of the bus landed in a heap, both pieces skidded along the highway and came to a stop. Smoke rose from the burning seats and bodies. There were cries of agony and loss as the surviving passengers looked for their family members many of which were dead or badly injured. The bomb had killed twenty-six civilians including seven children with eight more riders severely wounded and three missing.

The sapper was pleased with the results. The timing of the explosion was perfect. The Viet Cong terrorized the civilian population with bombings. They wanted to show the people that the South Vietnamese government could not protect them. The tactic was surprisingly effective as the civilians blamed the government and not the communists. Viet Cong recruitment increased from the villages near the attack. The young men and women joining the Viet Cong often did so because they saw the government troops as useless and downtrodden while the Viet Cong were powerful, and their morale was high. They wanted to be on the winning side when the dust finally settled.

Khe Sanh, South Vietnam

The shadow of a Cessna O-1 Bird Dog glided over the muddy water of the rice paddies below. The villagers were out in force replanting rice. The new seeds from the last harvest had already been planted on one side of the paddies and had grown the required three to six inches before being gently pulled up and replanted as seedlings six inches apart across the entire rice paddy. Planting rice by hand was almost as backbreaking as harvesting.

Inside the small aircraft, the pilot sat up front. There was no co-pilot. In the back, Karen sat on the lap of Gus Martin, a veteran AP war correspondent. Gus had been with the AP since the Indochina War. Near the end of the war, he married a young Vietnamese woman and had three children with her. They lived in Saigon where Gus worked. He was a good reporter and knew his way around the country, plus he had great contacts in the military. He was also fluent in Vietnamese which meant he didn't need a translator. It seemed like everyone knew Gus. Karen felt privileged to be assigned to him as his photographer for a story he was doing on the U.S. Army Engineers in the Central Highlands. Gus was a big man, and his thick legs made a good cushion for Karen's rump. "Gus says this is your first time in the field," said the pilot yelling over his shoulder.

"Yeah. I've been waiting for an assignment. I had no idea it took so long," said Karen.

"It doesn't usually," said Gus. "You just need to get to know the combat commanders and press officers in some of the units. Then you'll have your fill of assignments. Soldiers like to tell their stories and officers like the publicity for their units."

"I really appreciate you taking me along with you, Gus."

"I'm glad to have you. My regular guy fell out of a helicopter as it was landing and banged up his leg."

"I'll remember not to do that."

"Sometimes you can't help it. Huey pilots don't like to land if they're under fire. They want to keep moving. They'll tell you to jump out when the skids are still ten feet off the ground."

"And do you… jump?"

"Not very well. If it happens to you just bend your knees and go limp like landing with a parachute. Gravity will take care of the rest."

Karen laughed. She liked Gus and valued his advice. "The base is coming up on our left," said the pilot. "Hang on tight when we land. The runway isn't finished yet and still has a few potholes."

Karen looked out the side window at the Special Forces base below known as Khe Sanh. It was a key outpost that allowed SOG forces to easily penetrate Laos and scout planes to keep tabs on the Ho Chi Minh Trail. The engineers were busy expanding the base runway and preparing additional defensive positions. Westmoreland had decided that Khe Sanh needed more manpower if it was going to survive. The U.S. Marines were coming, and the base needed to be strengthened before their arrival.

After some prodding by MACV, the AP agreed to do a story on the U.S. Amy engineers. Khe Sanh seemed like the perfect story and Gus had gobbled it up after Peter Arnett had turned it down so he could do a story on the 101st Airborne Division. Gus had done a story on SOG before and knew several of the unit commanders at the base. They trusted him to tell a good story about their operators and keep his mouth shut about the secret stuff. Gus also knew that the SOG guys would appreciate seeing Karen and her long legs. It had been a while since they had seen an American woman. They were a rough bunch but well-mannered and a bit shy around women, especially American women.

The landing was bumpy just as the pilot had predicted and Karen bounced up and down on Gus's lap. The Cessna only needed fifty yards to take off or land which made it ideal for Khe Sanh's runway. At that point, Khe Sanh wasn't much more than a short runway and a few temporary buildings. The SOG had moved its headquarters to a nearby French fort that had been abandoned at the end of the Indochina War. The new Marine headquarters were to be located in the expanded Khe Sanh combat base.

Seven tractors were busy clearing away the jungle and foliage surrounding the base. During an inspection of their new home, the Marine commanders had requested long fields of fire to protect the base and the engineers were doing their damnedest to make that happen. Construction teams were building blockhouses with reinforced roofs to withstand enemy mortar and artillery shells. Building materials and supplies were stacked up everywhere. More were being flown in daily. It felt more like a construction site than a firebase. All that would change once the Marines had arrived and the enemy began its assaults. Its location made it probable that there would be one hell of a fight on both sides. The North Vietnamese and Viet Cong never got too possessive about any territory preferring to fight on their terms and where they wanted. But Khe Sanh was different. The Khe Sanh combat base was very much in the North Vietnamese and Viet Cong's faces, daring them to attack and threatening their lines of communication if they didn't. The base protected Highway 9 which was the only allied supply route in the area.

"Have the engineers give me a call on the radio when you're ready to be picked up," said the pilot as he braked to a stop.

"You're not staying?" said Karen a bit concerned.

"No. The VC may take potshots at the aircraft if it sits too long."

Karen and Gus got out of the aircraft. The pilot turned the plane around and took off. Karen immediately started taking photographs. "Don't you want to get the lay of the land before you start using up your film?" said Gus.

"I brought plenty of film," said Karen.

"Suit yourself, but I'd focus on the engineers. They're the story."

"Got it. I'll make sure you have plenty of options for your article."

Captain Vince Michaels, the commander of the engineer company greeted them and showed them around. "Where's the latrine?" said Karen.

"We had to tear it down to make room for the runway. We're building another. It should be done by tomorrow," said the captain.

"So, where does one relieve oneself?"

"Anywhere one wants."

"Seriously?"

"Yeah, there're piss tubes on the far end of the runway, but I don't imagine those will do you much good."

"So, just anywhere?"

"Well, preferably not where anyone walks a lot."

"Is there anywhere that is a little more private?"

"The jungle, but that's where the Viet Cong are hiding."

"Okay, so… not the jungle."

"There's a stack of corrugated metal just off to your left. Why don't you try behind there?"

"Thanks."

Karen moved off behind the stack of corrugated metal setting her camera on top of the stack. She realized that her jumpsuit required her to remove the top half in order to lower the bottom half. If it was good enough for Dickey, it's good enough for me, she thought and removed the top half exposing her bra. She was just about ready to squat when a bulldozer picked up the stack of metal sheets and swung it around. The fact that Karen was now exposed to the soldiers working nearby was less concerning than her camera being carried away. With her jumpsuit around her ankles, she hopped after the stack of metal and grabbed her camera.

A dozen soldiers stopped working to observe the spectacle. The only thing that saved her from complete embarrassment was an enemy mortar round that exploded in the middle of the base splintering a pile of railroad ties and sending shards of sharp wood through the air. The soldiers scrambled for cover. Karen was terrified. She pulled up her jumpsuit as she ran for the nearest trench. Diving into the trench, she landed on top of an engineer. Gus and Captain Michaels were in the same trench crouched down to keep heads below the top of the trench. Another shell exploded nearby.

The ground trembled. "Those are 120mm mortar rounds," said the captain to one of the engineers. "Intelligence said there wouldn't be anything above an 80," said the engineer. "We're gonna need to strengthen the blockhouse and bunker roofs."

"What should we do?" said Karen to Gus.

"I'd keep my head down," said Gus. "...and maybe snap a few photos."

"Okay."

Karen set her focus ring on infinity and held the camera above the trench exposing her hand but not her head. She snapped a photo, wound the camera, and snapped another as a round exploded showering them with dirt clods. "How long does this go on?" said Karen.

Hard to say," said the engineer. "But usually no more than four or five minutes. Depends on how much ammunition they have."

"Are they gonna attack?"

"I doubt it. They just wanna keep us on our toes. They do this a couple of times a week, but usually lighter rounds. Never the heavy stuff like this."

"So, what does that mean?"

"I don't know. Maybe they're getting serious and want to destroy the airfield before the Marines arrive."

"Can they do that with mortars?"

"A high-explosive 120 mm round can make a pretty good-sized crater in the runway but those are easy to fill in and compress. They'll do their best, but so will we. By the way, you wanna keep your mouth open a little during a mortar or artillery attack. It'll keep you from breaking an eardrum or hemorrhaging an eyeball among other things."

"Go to know. Do you mind if I take your photo?"

"No. Go ahead. Maybe my mom will see it. What newspaper do you work for?"

"All of them. I'm with Associated Press," said Karen as she snapped his photo, then wound the camera to take another.

"Should I smile?"

"No. Just look natural and don't look into the camera. It looks more real and has a better chance of being picked up."

She snapped another photo of the engineer looking serious and said, "Why don't they send some guys out to get 'em?"

"They will, but it's always too late. It's one of the reasons the VC like mortars over artillery. They can get in close, fire off a few rounds, then pack up the mortar and leave before we counterattack."

"They're smart… the Viet Cong."

"They're really smart, but so are we."

More mortar rounds exploded nearby. Every time a shell exploded, the trench walls would crumble a bit and the dust would rise. "You believe we are gonna win this thing?" said Karen.

"I wouldn't be here if I didn't," said the engineer. "This is my second tour. I got a wife and two kids waiting at home."

"You got pictures?"

"Now?"

"They'll keep my mind off the shelling."

As another shell exploded, the engineer pulled his wallet out and showed her the photos of his family. The shelling stopped. They both laughed. "Magic," said Karen. "You think it's safe to climb out?"

"Give it another minute, then go. Charlie can be really tricky sometimes."

"Thanks for the advice."

"I gotta keep you alive to get my photo in the newspaper, right?"

"Right."

Karen poked her head above the trench and snapped a few photos of soldiers climbing out from behind cover and out of trenches. It was good stuff. Far different than any photos she had taken before. This was life and death.

Waiting a minute, she climbed out of the trench and walked around. She could hear a soldier yelling in pain. She moved to where the sound was coming from and found a medic tending to a soldier that was bleeding heavily. The medic ripped open the soldier's pants exposing the wound just an inch away from the man's scrotum. Blood was pumping out of the two-inch gash. Karen felt dizzy. She forced herself to keep shooting. One shot after the other. She doubted any newspaper would buy such carnage, but her photos were about more than that. They were about history, and she wanted to do the moment justice. The soldier's eyes rolled back into his skull, and he stopped breathing. "Fuck," said the medic as he tied off the soldier's bleeding artery with his belt and moved to perform CPR.

It was no use. The soldier was dead. Karen was shocked and her hands trembled as she held her camera. The soldier's life has slipped away before her very eyes. Her eyes welled up with tears, but she kept snapping photo after photo changing the angle of the close-ups, then stepping back to a wide shot of the dead soldier and the medic trying to pump life back into the man. Suddenly, the soldier gasped, and Karen gasped with him. He was alive but barely. The medic stopped CPR and called out, "Little help here."

Several soldiers ran over and picked up the wounded soldier and carried him away towards the combat base hospital as the medic continued to work on him, keeping him alive. Karen snapped her last photo of the roll. She quickly rewound the film, opened the back of the camera, and pulled out the canister. She tucked it in her jumpsuit pocket and pulled out another roll. But it never made it into the camera. Her hands were shaking violently. She was overwhelmed and collapsed to the ground. It was all too much. She wept. Gus walked over and knelt down beside her. She grabbed him like she was holding on for dear life. Gus held her and said, "Welcome to the war, kid."

Saigon, South Vietnam

The next day, Karen flew back to Saigon. When she arrived at the Associated Press office, she immediately went to the photo lab to develop her film. She wasn't sure if anything she shot was useful. She handed the rolls to the darkroom technician. She wanted to go inside and supervise the development but knew that could be taken as an insult which was the last thing she wanted to do with the guy that would be handling her film. Instead, she sat outside and waited, bouncing her knees up and down like a 6th grader with too much pent-up energy.

A half-hour later, the technician came out and handed her a folder with twelve photos. "You should show those to the boss," said the technician before diving back into his dark hole. Karen waited a moment to steady herself, then opened the folder and looked inside. One of the photos that she snapped blindly during the mortar attack was of a soldier running toward the camera holding his helmet on his head to keep it from falling off. In the background was the explosion of a 120 mm mortar shell. It was all in perfect focus. She couldn't believe it. She lucked out. She leafed through the rest of the photos and found one of the medics giving CPR to the badly wounded soldier that had died and was brought back to life. The focus was perfect, and the light was dramatic. She grinned. At that moment, Browne left his office and walked past Karen. "Are those your shots from yesterday?" said Browne almost not stopping.

"Yeah," said Karen.

"Has Gus seen 'em?"

"Not yet. I just had them developed."

"Take 'em to my office and wait. I'll grab Gus on my way back and we'll look at them together."

"Okay."

Browne entered the men's bathroom. Karen closed the folder and walked into his office. She stood in front of Browne's desk. She had not been invited to sit yet and decided against it. The desk was a complete mess, covered with typewritten stories and photo contact sheets. She set her folder down adding to the mess. Various paperweights kept the overhead fan from blowing the papers onto the floor. Moving closer to one of the paperweights, a large golden coin, she recognized it as Browne's Pulitzer Prize. Most journalists never came close to winning one in their lifetime, and yet there it was, lying on his desk for any passerby to steal. She wanted to touch it and reached out... "He thinks it's cool just to leave it lying about," said Gus standing behind her. "Go ahead and pick it up. He won't mind."

"I just want to touch it," said Karen.

"No, you don't. You wanna see how heavy it is. Everyone does."

"Yeah, I do."

"You'll hate yourself if you don't. Once in a lifetime opportunity."

She considered for a moment, then picked it. Driven by the whirling fan, papers flew everywhere. Gus laughed. Karen set the medal back down and scrambled to collect the fallen paperwork. Gus helped her. Browne walked in, saw the mess, and said, "I really need a proper paperweight."

"Serves you right," said Gus.

"Where are your photos?" said Browne moving around them to sit behind his desk.

"In the folder," said Karen pointing.

Browne grabbed the folder and opened it. He poured through the photos and stopped on the photo of the mortar exploding with the soldier running toward the camera. "Nice," said Browne.

"Yeah, I like that one too," said Karen as if her opinion mattered. "Honestly, it was just luck. I couldn't even see through the viewfinder."

Browne handed the photo to Gus. "Nice," said Gus.

Browne moved through the photos until he came to the photos of the medic performing CPR. He looked down at the image and said, "Incredible tension. Did he live?"

"I think so. He was breathing again when they took him away," said Karen.

"Huh," said Browne. "Gus, when are you gonna finish your story on the engineers?"

"I'm almost done. Maybe a few more hours to polish," said Gus.

"Give it to me. I'll polish it. I want you to write another story about what it's like to be under fire."

"I could do that."

"Congratulations. We're gonna send both of these photos out on the wire along with Gus's new story and see who bites," said Browne.

"Really?"

"Really."

"Beginner's luck."

"I always say I'd rather be lucky than smart. Both of you get out of my office. You're making a mess." Gus and Karen rose and walked to the doorway. "One last thing," said Browne pitching the Pulitzer Prize to Karen who fumbled it for a moment but didn't drop it. "Heavy, ain't it?"

WHITE WING

January 24, 1966 - Binh Dinh Province, South
Vietnam

The morning sky seemed filled with helicopters flying
in a loose formation. Ferried to Binh Dinh Province in
their personal armada of helicopters, U.S. 1st Calvary
Division was on the move again. This time as part of
Operation Masher, also called White Wing when
President Johnson asked that it be renamed with
something more benign. The area of operation was
spread out over hundreds of square miles. The
American forces were joined by the ARVN 22nd
Division and the South Korean Capital Division for a
combined force of 15,000 soldiers. It was the largest
search and destroy operation since the Americans had
arrived in Vietnam.

A recent CIA report had declared that the Binh
Dinh province and its 800,000 inhabitants were just
about lost to the communists. Westmoreland would
not stand for that. He wanted it back and was willing
to fight for it. He made it clear to the division
commanders that their troops needed to be aggressive
to defeat the Viet Cong and NVA in the area. He was

sending his best to make the point and expected his allies to do the same. Adjacent to Binh Dinh was Quang Ngai province where U.S. Marines and South Vietnamese Marines were carrying out a similar mission – Operation Double Eagle.

Binh Dinh Province was a narrow, heavily cultivated coastal plane with rivers separated by jungle-covered ridges and low mountains. There were plenty of places for the Viet Cong to hide and set ambushes. The main effort would be focused on the Bong Son Plain with its surrounding mountains and valleys. The narrow strip of land started at the town of Bong Son, then ran northward parallel to the coast. Inside the territory, there were a series of small deltas that led to rolling hills, then to mountainous spurs from the Highlands. The steep spurs held rivers in narrow valleys. The plain was divided by the Lai Giang River which was fed by the An Lao and Kim Son Rivers. While the wet season had ended in December, there was still a drizzle most days interspersed with torrential downpours for which the area was known. The overcast skies and weather would at times limit air support making it dangerous territory to tangle with the Viet Cong and NVA.

Highway 1 ran north and south through Binh Dinh and was considered a vital artery. The area of operation was thirty miles inland from the South China Sea, out of range of the American naval guns. Additional artillery was carried into the area by helicopters to provide extra support when airpower was not available.

The Americans, Koreans, and South Vietnamese were facing the NVA 3rd Division and one regiment of Viet Cong guerrillas totaling a little over 6,000 enemy soldiers. In their ranks were experienced fighters that had fought the French and the South Vietnamese forces for over a decade. The majority of the population in Binh Dinh supported the communists and many villages hid food, ammunition, and weapons for the soldiers.

The plan for the task force was for the U.S., South Vietnamese, and Korean troops in Operation White Wing to sweep north while the U.S. and South Vietnamese Marines in Operation Double Eagle swept south. The opposing direction of the two forces was meant to catch and grind the fleeing NVA and Viet Cong soldiers killing them. While the purpose of the two operations was to officially restore the South Vietnamese government in the area by driving out the communist, the primary metric for judging the success of the operations would be the body count of the enemy soldiers killed.

The campaign was broken into two parts. The first part was a deception operation. A brigade-size task force would establish a command and supply base at Phu Cat on Highway 1 south of the real area of operations. Hopefully, the enemy would see this as their enemy's main objective and reposition their troops to destroy the base.

The second part of the campaign would move division-sized elements to Bong Son and launch a series of 1st Cav Airmobile hammer and anvil operations on the plain itself. The idea was to flush the NVA and VC units toward strong blocking positions where they could be pinned down, then easily destroyed with artillery and airpower. The U.S. commander in charge of the White Wing Operation was General Harry Kinnard. He assigned Colonel Hal Moore and his 3rd Brigade to drive and chase the enemy into the killing zones. 3rd Brigade had taken heavy casualties in the Ia Drang valley battle and was still not up to full strength. Nevertheless, Moore took on the mission with his usual gusto. He assigned the 1st Battalion, 7th Calvary commanded by Lieutenant Colonel Raymond Kampe, and the 1st Battalion, 12th Calvary commanded by Lieutenant Colonel Rutland Beard to take up positions in Phu Cat where they would secure the airfield and support base. Once joined by the South Korean battalions, the Americans would take the lead in wide-ranging search & destroy missions. Lieutenant Colonel Robert McDade's 2nd Battalion, 7th Calvary had been ordered to Bong Son by plane, then helicopter to Landing Zone Dog.

After loading up in a dozen C-123 Providers the battalion took off for a short flight to Bong Son. In the mountains near An Khe, one of the transport aircraft crashed killing the four crewmen and forty-two soldiers on board. It was a heavy blow to the 2nd Battalion which was already below strength. The rest of the Battalion landed in Bong Son without further incident, but morale was expectedly lowered. Once helicoptered to LZ Dog, the engineers started building an airstrip and digging in the Battalion's artillery.

On the second wave of transport helicopters, Karen along with several other war correspondents and photojournalists flew inside a CH-47 Chinook carrying ammunition and supplies. White Wing was a massive operation and there would be plenty of work to go around for the journalists. But the fact that Karen, a rookie had made the list, turned heads in the AP office.

She got the plum assignment because Coyle had kept his word and arranged for her to be embedded with 1st Calvary. Secretly, Coyle thought Karen would be safer as part of a large operation surrounded by thousands of American soldiers rather than a small patrol in the jungle. He was still her father and had no desire to endure the wrath of her mother if Karen got hurt.

Also riding in a Huey as part of the second wave was Granier and his newly chosen Keyman team. They didn't have a particular target. Instead, Granier hoped to run them through their paces and make sure they were up to the task at hand. The team was made up of a two-man sniper unit, a translator/interrogator, a demolitions specialist, and two heavy weapons specialists, one carrying an M60 machine gun and the other carrying the cases of ammunition the weapon chewed through like corn on the cob on the 4th of July.

When the Chinook landed and Karen stepped out, she saw Granier already on the Landing Zone assembling his team and their gear. She recognized him from the embassy, a soldier without any insignia on his uniform. His team also lacked insignia on their camouflaged uniforms. "Why don't they have insignia on their uniforms?" Karen asked one of the other journalists getting out of the chopper.

"Probably CIA. But they won't tell you if they are. They'll just grunt."

Karen was intrigued. He was dangerous and mysterious. That made him even more attractive.

Granier felt someone was watching him as he and his team moved off the landing zone. He looked back at the landing zone and saw Karen with her camera around her neck. She was an attractive young photojournalist wearing a jumpsuit and combat boots. He liked the jumpsuit. It made her look woodsy, yet feminine. She smiled at him. The smile unhinged him a bit as he disappeared into the surrounding bush along with the rest of the team. Granier did not flirt with women or try to catch their attention in any shape or form. He found women to be a pain in the ass. They talked too much and always needed attention. He didn't have time to play their games and had no desire to impress them. And yet… she smiled at him. Being distracted in enemy territory could get him or the team he commanded killed. Evil woman.

With his Brigade in place, Moore was ready to carry out his search & destroy mission to the east of the mountains when a Chinook CH-47 was shot down by the Viet Cong just north of Bong Son at Landing Zone Papa. Moore sent a company from 1/7th Calvary to secure the crash site and rescue the survivors. On its way to the LZ, the company came under heavy enemy fire and was pinned down.

Moore ordered the rest of the battalion to reinforce the besieged company, but by the time they arrived the Viet Cong had disengaged and disappeared into the countryside. This was a common pattern: ambushing their enemy, then retreating before reinforcements could arrive or airpower and artillery could come into play. They would sting their enemy but not kill it as the cost to do so was too high. This brought great frustration to the allied battalion commanders as they were unable to rack up a decent body count if the VC or NVA didn't stand their ground. Body count, not captured territory or control of the battlefield, was how victory was measured by the Americans. The body count was what Secretary of Defense McNamara wanted for his IBM computer. The body count was something that could be measured. The only problem was that body count was being exaggerated more and more as the war dragged on. Civilians were often labeled as Viet Cong to increase the body count of an operation. A high body count looked good on a commander's reports to MACV. It didn't seem to matter if it was a lie. Everyone knew that the truth was more flexible during wartime.

American firebases Brass and Steel were stepped up to support the battalions in the areas of operation. Lieutenant Colonel McDade's Company C, 2/7th was deployed by helicopter to Landing Zone 4 next to the hamlet of Phung Du 2. Company C had omitted the artillery barrage that usually prepared a landing site because of its proximity to the village. The first skids of troops landed without incident, and they formed a defensive perimeter securing the landing zone. When the second skids arrived ten minutes later, all hell broke loose. The NVA 7th Battalion, 22nd Regiment was scattered throughout the hamlet's entrenched earthworks and bunkers. They opened fire with machine guns and mortars on the Americans as the helicopters were about to land. Company C's commander, Captain Fesmire, waved off the helicopters. Seeing the company under fire, the helicopter pilots landed at four different locations nearby and dropped off their troops. Returning to the hamlet ten minutes later with the third lift, the pilots dropped off their troops at yet another location. The Company was spread out and under fire at six different locations. Under intense enemy fire and being unable to maneuver to support one another, the Americans were forced to fight in defragmented positions. To make matters worse, it began to rain heavily which impeded air support. Because the Americans were so dispersed and their locations were unknown to one another, artillery was of little use. They were on their own against an entrenched enemy force and pinned down. American casualties began mounting quickly.

Realizing that his men were being wiped out, McDade ordered A Company to reinforce C Company. When A Company reached Landing Zone 4, they too came under intense enemy fire. They formed their own defensive perimeter using rice paddy dikes for cover but were unable to reach C Company.

Six more helicopters carrying reinforcements from Company B reached LZ 4 and immediately came under heavy enemy ground fire. All six helicopters were hit. Two of the helicopters were unable to land and were driven off. The remaining four landed and their troops were deployed. They too came under intense crossfire and did little to help the situation. McDade joined Company A, but there was little he could do. The company was still pinned down and could not maneuver to assist Company C. He was able to call some artillery strikes on the enemy positions which took a little pressure off Company C whose only real hope was darkness.

When the sun finally set, the troops in Company C were able to consolidate their position in the darkness and heavy rain. But McDade wasn't satisfied and ordered Fesmire to move his company to the south and link up with the other companies.

The troops in Company C carried twenty wounded and the bodies of eight soldiers that had been killed. At 4:30 AM, Company C linked up with the troops in A and B companies and helped form a battalion defensive perimeter. Everyone was exhausted but were able to catch an hour of sleep before the sun rose once again and the heavy fighting resumed. Fortunately for the Americans, the low overcast sky had lifted, and fighter-bombers were able to join the fight. The warplanes pounded the NVA positions in and around the hamlet. Bombs and rockets detonated the NVA's ammunition depot causing a huge explosion and spreading fires throughout the village.

When the 2nd Battalion, 12th Calvary arrived to reinforce McDade's battalion, Granier and his team arrived with them. Granier put his sniper and heavy weapons teams to work targeting enemy unit commanders. Granier trailed behind and observed as his team worked its way toward the enemy lines and cut the head off the snake. They were experienced operators and killed efficiently. In all, two enemy officers and six NCOs were killed by Granier's team creating chaos within the NVA ranks. The Americans were able to clear the hamlet of NVA forces. Granier was satisfied with his team's performance. They were the best soldiers he had ever commanded, and he felt confident they could carry out Keyman operations successfully.

The NVA had lost 566 soldiers while the Americans had 123 dead which included the forty-six soldiers killed in the C-123 crash. In addition, two helicopters were shot down and twenty-nine were damaged. It was hardly an allied victory, but General Kinnard, the operation commander, declared it one anyway.

Karen and the other journalists were flown in by helicopter to witness the battlefield. She wound her way through the hamlet shrouded in smoke from the fires snapping photos as she walked. An American soldier had a bag full of candy that he was handing out to the children in the burning village. In the background were two dead civilians lying on the ground. Karen took the photo. Shafts of sunlight filtered by the smoke made the photo both beautiful and horrific. An old woman walked up to her and said something in Vietnamese that Karen didn't understand. She asked one of the other journalists to translate. "She is asking if you are the French," said the journalist.

Karen shook her head and the old woman moved off. It was surreal and the smell of burning human flesh mixed with animal flesh made Karen sick to her stomach. The image of BBQ skewers of an unknown meat roasting over a hibachi flashed in her mind. She went around the corner of a hut and vomited until there was nothing left in her stomach. It would be a long time until she could eat a hamburger again and then only if it was well done. Feeling slightly better, she went back to work taking photos.

As Granier and his team were boarding a helicopter, he looked back at the village. Through the smoke, he saw Karen. She was no longer smiling as she took photos of what remained of the hamlet and the survivors. Granier wondered if he would ever see her again. The pull this strange woman had on him felt odd. He didn't like it. It weakened him. He climbed in the chopper and the pilot took off. Smoke swirled into vortices as the helicopter's blades sliced through the grayish-brown air above the smoldering village.

Operation White Wing continued with missions in the An Lao Valley, the Kim Son Valley, and Cay Giap Mountains. The fighting displaced 140,000 refugees leaving their villages and hamlets for safer territory while the two sides slugged it out with air strikes, artillery bombardments, and ground forces.

The United States believed that supplying humanitarian needs to the refugees was the responsibility of the South Vietnam government. The government's response was inefficient and inadequate in what was needed to tend to the sick and wounded. Housing and food were also major shortfalls for such a large number of refugees. The South Vietnamese leaders did the bare minimum to provide scenes of hope for the public relations photos for the media. For most politicians and generals, creating positive impressions was more important than actually doing something for the refugees in South Vietnam. Events of handing out food and medicine were staged and quickly disappeared once the photojournalists were gone. Karen always took her time when taking photos at staged events, knowing that more food and medicine would be given out to the people in need. Her sluggishness often pissed off the South Vietnamese handlers that had staged the events. She didn't care if they were angry. She didn't work for them.

Even so, the Americans considered the entire operation a success. They had demonstrated the capabilities of 1st Calvary Airmobile in conducting a sustained campaign to find, fix, and finish the enemy forces. 171 B-52 strikes and 132,000 artillery shells pounded suspected enemy positions. It was a massive use of artillery and air power. In addition, the

Americans provided tactical air support with over 600 sorties. The U.S. claimed 1,342 NVA and VC killed while the ARVN and Korean forces claimed an additional 808 enemy killed. Over 500 NVA and VC were taken prisoner.

On the other side, the NVA claimed victory claiming they had killed over 2,000 enemy troops and had avoided destruction by a much larger force. The truth was somewhere in between.

It was estimated that six civilians died for every soldier killed. The U.S. claimed the Viet Cong were responsible for the high civilian death toll because of the VC tactics of firing from populated areas such as inside and around villages. Despite the size of the operation, most of the NVA and Viet Cong forces had escaped and were able to return to the area a few months later. Two months after the conclusion of White Wing, 1st Calvary was back in Operation Crazy Horse and sweep much of the same area attempting to drive away the enemy permanently. Then once again with Operation Thayer to fully pacify Binh Dinh Province. Neither worked in the long term and Binh Dinh continued to be a hot spot of communism throughout the war.

White House, Washington D.C., USA

The Vietnam War continued to have wide support among the American people, but cracks in that support were starting to show as more protests were televised and many intellectuals on political talk shows argued the war should end. As usual, the political environment followed the voting public, and the vast majority of senators and congressmen voiced their support for the war. Senator John Sherman Cooper was not one of them.

President Johnson had accepted the one-on-one meeting with Cooper. He liked Cooper and saw him as a straight shooter. Johnson had selected Cooper as a member of the Warren Commission to investigate the assassination of President Kennedy. Cooper did not agree with the final report of the Warren Commission given to Johnson and told him so. Cooper did not believe that Oswald had acted alone and said, "…it's important for this nation that we bring the true murderers to justice." While somewhat skeptical himself, Johnson wanted the nation to move on and focus on other things. He accepted the Warren Commission's findings.

Cooper had supported Johnson's Gulf of Tonkin resolution giving the president expanded powers to prosecute the war but had grown disillusioned with the war as more American troops, advisors, and pilots were killed and the expenditure of the war seemed to balloon every year.

Cooper sat down with Johnson in the oval office. Drinking coffee, they reminisced about Johnson's time in the senate as the senate majority leader. Johnson wanted to get down to brass tacks and said, "So, John, what's on your mind?"

"Mr. President, I've been told you are seriously considering resuming the bombing of North Vietnam."

"You are not wrong, John. I gave those people a chance to negotiate a peaceful end to the war and all I got was crickets."

"I won't expect negotiations with communists to be easy."

"Negotiations? Hell, I can't even get 'em to the table, let alone negotiate with 'em."

"You need to give it more time, Mr. President."

"We don't have any more time. The Pentagon was furious when a halt to the bombing was even suggested. Now, those generals are downright rude in their criticisms of me to the press."

"If you restart the bombing, you will destroy whatever progress you have made."

"I haven't made any progress, John. It's hopeless. The only thing Hanoi understands is force and I intend to show them the force of the U.S. Military as they have never seen it before."

"This war is not going to end well for America, Mr. President."

"I think you might be right on that count, John. But I see no other way than to press forward and win."

"A lot of our boys are gonna die and you could bankrupt our nation trying to prove your point."

"It's not my point. I didn't start this war, but I sure as hell am gonna finish it. The American public wants to move on with issues here at home and that's exactly what I am going to give them. But first, we gotta win this war and bring our boys home."

"Those that survive."

Johnson went silent for almost a minute. Cooper could see that he had pushed the president too far. Johnson finally broke the silence and said, "It's good of you to stop by and chat, John. Please give my love to Lorraine."

"Of course. Thank you for your time, Mr. President."

Johnson walked the senator out of the oval office and closed the door. He had held his temper.

January 31, 1966 – North Vietnam

After a thirty-seven-day hiatus, Operation Rolling Thunder resumed aerial bombardment of the North by order of the president. The first target was the bridge at Dong Hoi just past the demilitarized zone. American B-52 bombers blew the bridge and the surrounding area to smithereens. It was overkill, but the Americans wanted to make a big splash to send a message to the North; the U.S. Air Force was back in business. The destruction of the bridge was complete, and it would take North Vietnamese engineers and laborers several weeks before it was operational once again.

Rolling Thunder had four main objectives: boost morale in the South Vietnamese government; persuade North Vietnam to cease their support of the Viet Cong; destroy North Vietnam's transportation network, industrial base, and air defenses; and finally, halt the flow of men and supplies to South Vietnam. But President Johnson and the White House put restrictions on the military by determining what is and what is not a legitimate target for bombing. The Johnson administration wanted to hold down the number of civilian casualties and wanted to prevent the Chinese from entering the war. Even the type and number of aircraft used, the tonnages allowed, and the day and hour of the bombardments were determined by the White House. Nothing was spur of the moment and the missions were often selected by committee. Airstrikes were forbidden within thirty miles of Hanoi and within ten miles of the port of Haiphong where Russian and Chinese freighters were unloaded. There was also a thirty-mile buffer zone along the Chinese border with North Vietnam. Because of the number of Chinese and Soviet advisors training the North Vietnamese Air Force, airfields in the north were also off the target list.

Johnson and McNamara wanted to keep a tight rein on the military to prevent the war from expanding further. The American pilots were further stifled by the military aid and assistance received by North Vietnam from communist allies, China, the Soviet Union, and North Korea. With their help, North Vietnam fielded MiG fighter-interceptor jets and technically advanced air-to-air and surface-to-air weapons. These weapons formed the most effective air defenses the American aviators had ever faced.

It was believed by the White House that the doctrine of gradualism should be the overall strategy of the Rolling Thunder Campaign. The Americans would hold back the bombing of important targets and keep them as hostages while bombing trivial targets to show their determination. That was the problem with Washington's thinking, they believed the North Vietnamese would react rationally to more force. But the North Vietnamese did not think like the westerners. They were far more idealistic and passionate about their cause. They would never give up as long as Vietnam was divided. They were determined to fly the communist flag over Saigon.

Except for the B-52s which were based in Guam, the majority of sorties during Rolling Thunder were launched from four air bases in Thailand: Korat, Takhli, Udorn, and Ubon. The aircraft were refueled over Laos by air tankers before crossing the border and attacking their targets in North Vietnam. To limit airspace conflicts, the Pentagon divided North

Vietnam into six target regions called "route packages." Each route package was assigned to either the U.S. Navy or the U.S. Air Force and into which the other was forbidden to fly. The Navy strikes were launched from aircraft carriers positioned off the coast at Yankee Station in the Gulf of Tonkin. Naval aircraft carried lighter bomb loads and had shorter ranges than their air force cousins. The Naval aviators approached most of their targets by flying over the coastline.

The Joint Chiefs persuaded McNamara and Johnson to allow a four-week assault focused on enemy lines of communications in the north. About one-third of North Vietnam's supply shipments from the Soviets and China were transported on the Hanoi-Lao Cai railway from China, while two-thirds of weapons and supplies arrived by sea through Haiphong Harbor and other ports. MACV wanted to cut off the land supply line. During the air assault, the Americans destroyed twenty-six bridges and seven ferries. They also destroyed North Vietnamese radar systems, barracks, and ammunition depots.

McNamara and Johnson were impressed by the results and gave the go-ahead to expand the assaults. MACV changed the missions from fixed targets to reconnaissance-type missions where small groups of aircraft would patrol highways, railroads, and rivers in the north and search for targets of opportunity. It was a success and eventually, seventy-five percent of the bombing undertakings were reconnaissance-type missions. It was the pilots that were making the decisions of what and when to attack, not the White House. McNamara and Johnson were fine with that as long as the assaults produced results and didn't start World War III with the Chinese and Russians.

The bombing campaign targeting North Vietnam was not without problems. The biggest of which was the layers of decision-makers required to approve any mission in North Vietnam or Laos. As head of MACV, Westmoreland had the ultimate say so on all missions including the U.S. Air Force and the Navy. Westmoreland wanted the bombing missions to focus on cutting supplies and reinforcements to Central South Vietnam where the NVA and Viet Cong were strongest and most active. CINPAC in Honolulu, Hawaii was more focused on destroying infrastructure around Hanoi and along the coast. To make matters even more complicated, the U.S. Ambassadors in Thailand and Laos had veto power on any missions launched or executed from their respective countries. And, of course, the final authority rested with Secretary of Defense McNamara and President Johnson. Everybody wanted their say so before any mission was authorized which made the process slower than a sloth crossing a road. By converting the missions to reconnaissance-type flights where the pilots determined the targets, the bombing campaign decision-making process was vastly improved and proved more effective.

Since the North Vietnamese had little hope of matching American air power, they switched their defense strategy to air deniability. In less than a year, the North Vietnamese with help from their allies increased the number of anti-aircraft guns from 1,500 to over 5,000 including 85 and 100mm radar-directed weapons. During Rolling Thunder, eighty percent of American aircraft losses came from anti-aircraft fire.

In addition to the anti-aircraft defenses, the North

Vietnamese increased its number of fighter aircraft from fifty-three in 1965 to over 100 in 1966. While the majority of communist aircraft were MiG-17s, later in the year MiG-21s began to make their presence known in the skies above North Vietnam. The MiG-21s were more comparable in weaponry and performance to the American fighters. The North Vietnamese kept most of their interceptors on airfields across the border in China where they could not be attacked by American aircraft.

North Vietnam's most crucial resource was its people, sometimes known as the "Ant Army." Hundreds of thousands of civilians were put to work repairing bomb damage caused by the Americans. When North Vietnam's lines of communications came under attack, truck convoys and supply trains were divided into smaller elements that only traveled at night. When bridges were destroyed, the ant army built dirt fords, pontoon ferries, and underwater bridges that were durable and easily repaired as the air assaults continued. Citizens used Sampans, reinforced bicycles, wheelbarrows, and carts to keep the supplies and weapons moving. Slogans like "Each kilogram of goods is a bullet into the head of the American pirates," kept the people motivated.

Things changed in 1966 for American air operations when the North Vietnamese deployed more SAM-2s to shoot down U.S. aircraft. The American aviators faced hard choices as they continued to carry out their bombing missions. They could fly low to avoid the SAMs and become the targets of anti-aircraft guns or they could fly high and expose their aircraft to ground-to-air missiles. With the introduction of more missile sites, American aircraft casualties rose dramatically. North Vietnam had an estimated force of twenty-five SAM battalions with six missile launchers each. To keep the Americans on their toes, the SAM battalions were rotated between 150 sites throughout the north.

The U.S. forces had to adapt new tactics to survive the communist missiles. The more prominent of these were Iron Hand flak suppression operations carried out before the bombers entered the target area. Iron Hand missions were made up of F-105 Wild Weasels. The aircraft of these hunter/killer teams were configured with sophisticated electronic equipment that could detect the enemy control radar installations that guided the SAM missiles and launchers. The aircraft carried AGM-45 Shrike anti-radiation missiles which homed in on the radar emissions coming from the SAM guidance systems. While the SAMs had greater range than the Shrikes, the enemy operating the guidance system would often be forced to choose between continuing to guide a missile that had been launched and risk being destroyed by an incoming Shrike or simply turning off their guidance systems. Most chose to turn off their radar whenever Wild Weasels were in the area. The Wild Weasels also carried electronic countermeasures to protect themselves. It was a wicked game of cat and mouse played above the skies in the north.

Other American fighters that escorted the bombers were outfitted with electronic jamming equipment that would degrade enemy radar used to detect the bombers or to throw mid-air missile guidance off if a SAM was fired.

The North Vietnamese with the help of the Soviets also developed new tactics to deal with the American electronic countermeasures. One of the techniques was to turn their radar to the side and turn it on briefly. The American pilots would see the radar signature and fire their Shrikes. When the enemy radar system was turned off, the Shrikes would lose contact and crash harmlessly.

During the war, the Soviets delivered ninety-five SA-2 systems to North Vietnam along with 7,658 missiles. Thirty-one percent of all American aircraft downed by the North Vietnamese were from SA missiles compared to only nine percent being shot down by MiG fighters. The SAM missile program was a great success for Hanoi, and they often paraded some of the missiles each year through downtown to boost morale.

Rolling Thunder evolved as more targets previously off-limits were authorized for destruction. However, Rolling Thunder did little to slow down the North Vietnamese who seemed to repair the damage from the air assaults within days or even hours. The Soviets and Chinese quickly replaced whatever weapons or supplies were lost by the American bombardments. It was a hopeless situation that the US military was reluctant to admit. They kept up the pressure by using more and more bombs that had little effect. It just didn't make sense to MACV and the Pentagon that a backward nation like North Vietnam could effectively defeat the air power of the United States. The generals could not admit that they were wrong even when it meant losing more pilots and air crews.

Saigon, South Vietnam

Granier had sent a cable to Bill saying, "Team is ready."

He was surprised by how quickly he was summoned to the U.S. Embassy where he received a large, sealed envelope. Inside, was a report on the Viet Cong's civilian infrastructure known as VCI.

After the 1954 Geneva Conference which split Vietnam in two, the North Vietnamese wasted no time in preparing for the upcoming elections that had been ordered by the Geneva Accords and would reunite the country under democratically elected leadership. Ho Chi Minh was the leading candidate and was expected to win by a landslide in both the north and the south. The North Vietnamese secretly contacted and organized thousands of communist political leaders in the south. These covert leaders were to arrange political rallies and form political organizations in the south before the election to ensure the communists took control of the country once it was reunited.

When then Prime Minister Ngo Dinh Diem realized that he would lose a general election to the popular and beloved Ho Chi Minh, he decided to have his own election in the south which he rigged. In a landslide election, Diem won ninety-seven percent of the vote, which was statistically impossible and declared himself president of a new South Vietnamese republic. In addition, Diem declared that the people of South Vietnam had voted for their independence and there was no need for a general election to reunite the two countries.

The disenfranchised voters in the south were furious and formed a covert insurgency that eventually became the Viet Cong. Its sole purpose was to undermine and destroy the South Vietnamese government, then reunite the south and the north under communist leadership based in Hanoi.

Over the years, the VCI had grown in size to over 150,000 political and military operatives throughout the south. Not all were fighters. Many were political agitators that encouraged the people in the countryside to rebel against the South Vietnamese government and resist the ARVN. It was estimated that the VCI controlled fifty to seventy percent of the population outside the large South Vietnamese cities. The VCI set up shadow governments in the south that would collect taxes, indoctrinate the local populations in the benefits of communism, and identify recruits for the Viet Cong forces in the area. The VCI leaders chose small villages because they lacked supervision from the South Vietnamese government or the ARVN.

The Keyman team's main targets would be the covert VCI operatives leading the people in the countryside astray. Through effective interrogation, the Keyman team would uncover the vast network of communist operatives in the south and destroy it.

Granier recognized that it was a huge task for such a small team. But he also knew that Operation Keyman was a pilot program and that if successful, would be expanded into something far more capable of tackling the VCI.

In addition to the report was a dossier on the team's first assignment - Ngo Duy Thach, a Saigon University medical graduate that had relocated to the Ben Tre Province in the Mekong Delta. Once there, he disappeared, presumably under an assumed name and identity. As part of the communist movement, he had liberated dozens of villages and organized a shadow government. Just sixty miles to the south of Saigon, Ben Tre had become a major staging area for Viet Cong assaults on ARVN outposts. While Thach's assassination would stir up the hornet's nest, it was considered essential to regaining government control of the area.

Granier decided the first part of the operation would be locating Thach. It wouldn't be easy. There was only one photo of Thach from when he was a medical student over eighteen years ago. Granier and the team reviewed all the available information on Thach. There wasn't much. Thach was an enigma that remained in perpetual hiding.

Granier had requested and received a large amount of cash to be used for the team's expenses and bribes to be used to locate targets. He had little hope that bribes would help in locating Thach. True communists cared little about money and were unusually loyal to their cause. Still, life was about change and at times even loyal communists had personal issues and might be tempted to accept a bribe to save face from financial ruin. The team would throw some money around and see what intel they could dig up on Thach's whereabouts.

Granier's translator and interrogator, Le Thai Sang was born in Lang Son next to the Chinese border. Her mother was the mistress of a French magistrate who was married and had a family in Leon, France. While her father never acknowledged her as his daughter, he did ensure that she was educated at the best schools in Hanoi. Although her native tongue was Vietnamese, as a child she had learned French and Mandarin, spoken by many of the people in the border city that profited from trade with the Chinese. Later, she learned Russian, Laotian, and English. She also spoke a little Khmer and some hill tribe dialects.

When the French lost the war and left Hanoi, she

and her mother traveled south. As the Americans took the place of the French in supporting South Vietnam, the CIA offered Sang a job translating and the opportunity to become an American citizen once the war was over. She took it and hoped to someday move to Colorado where it snowed. She had never touched snow but found the cold white flakes intriguing.

The CIA trained her in interrogation along with certain forms of torture. She was strangely good at both. As a female many of the male suspects were disarmed by her soft voice and attractive appearance. She could be both comforting and terrifying depending on the situation and detainee. She was surprisingly effective and was able to get some detainees to talk when other interrogators had failed.

The team's demolition specialist, Pham Viet Cuong had been born in the Mekong Delta and still had some contacts through his family and childhood friends. The problem was that he didn't know who had become a communist and who had not. He too had been recruited by the CIA after the Indochina War. He had served in the French Army where he learned to be an engineer which included explosive training. His English and French were good, and he had no problem blending in as a civilian anywhere in Vietnam. He also knew his way around a radio which could be helpful in calling in airstrikes if necessary.

The rest of the team were Americans. They were a mix of former special forces and airborne that had joined the CIA when their tours were up. The Vietnam War was where the action was, and they wanted to remain part of it. They wanted to make a difference and protect their country. They were patriots. The two heavy weapon specialists were Paul York and David

Fisher. The sniper team had Colton Rogers and Eliot Hammond.

Granier wanted the team members to be careful not to reveal the team's existence or purpose to Thach and the other communists in the area. He knew that some exposure would be necessary to find Thach. When the team moved into the city of Ben Tre, Granier made sure they traveled separately and stayed in different hotels or guest houses. He rented a small warehouse on the edge of the city in an abandoned industrial area. What the building lacked in esthetics with its cracked windows and a layer of dust on its concrete floor it made up for in privacy. They could meet when required without drawing any attention. Their covers were aid workers and entrepreneurs looking to start an export business. They dressed appropriately and even had business cards that matched their fake IDs. Each was given money to purchase a used motorbike or rent a car.

They gathered in the small warehouse to make a plan. "I'm open for suggestions on how to find Thach," said Granier.

"Thach was a medical student," said Sang. "He needed a cover. I wouldn't be surprised if he went to work in a medical clinic or hospital."

"Why not private practice?"

"It's possible, but a doctor is revered in our culture. He could use a clinic or hospital to recruit patients or associates. He would want to be around a lot of potential recruits."

"Alright. We need to check out clinics and hospitals in the area. What else?"

"I was thinking… he has been successful at converting a lot of civilians to the communist cause," said Hammond. "I don't think he could have produced those kinds of numbers converting people one on one."

"What do you mean?"

"He probably uses rallies or events to recruit en masse."

"That would be dangerous for him. The South Vietnamese counterintelligence officers watch for that kind of thing."

"And yet he's never been caught that we know of."

"...that we know of?"

"He might have been detained under his assumed name and identity or possibly another name."

"So, we look back through the counterintelligence interrogation records and see if we can find something."

"I don't think the local counterintelligence unit is going to just hand over their records because we say 'please.'"

"Let me worry about that. I'll get the records one way or another. What else?"

"Rabbit's feet. We need to get lucky," said Fisher.

"Don't be a smart ass," growled Granier. "We need to stay focused on the job at hand; finding Thach."

"What if we find someone, we think might be him but we're not sure?" said Rogers.

"If you put me in a room with him for two hours, I can determine his identity," said Sang.

"Are you sure?"

"Very."

"We'll jump off that bridge when we get to it. For now, all possible candidates should be brought to my attention," said Granier. "We leave no stone unturned."

Granier opened a folder and handed out copies of the only photo of Thach. The CIA had trained the team members on how to extrapolate the current appearance of a subject from an old photo. There was also a brief physical description including height and weight. Although his weight could have changed over time, it was doubtful Thach had increased or decreased his height. "Let's start putting the pieces together," said Granier. "I need an hour to think it through, then I'll give each of you your assignments."

After considering the situation and the plan, Granier decided that someone on the team needed to infiltrate the Viet Cong in the area. It would be the most dangerous assignment. He gave it to Cuong because of his contacts in the area. Granier went over Cuong's cover story multiple times until Cuong could answer questions without thinking. He assigned Rogers and Hammond to cover Cuong during his initial contact with the communists. As much as they could protect him, they could also endanger him if discovered. They would keep their distance but be prepared to move quickly if Cuong got into trouble.

Sang was assigned to investigate the clinics and hospitals. York and Fisher would set up surveillance and watch from the exterior. If Thach sensed something was wrong, he might try to run. Granier didn't want him slipping the noose. York and Fisher would be waiting. They would kill him if there was no other choice rather than to let him escape.

There weren't many clinics and even fewer hospitals in the Mekong Delta. A majority were staffed by foreign doctors and nurses. The Philippines had sent a large number of medical staff to South Vietnam in a show of support for the war effort. The Americans and French also manned medical facilities in the area. It was a surprisingly dangerous occupation to be a doctor or a nurse in communist territory. The Viet Cong saw the medical community as a hindrance to their efforts and often kidnapped doctors. Many were disappeared while others were returned safely when a ransom was paid.

Dressed in a white blouse and dark grey suit usually worn by government officials, Sang carried a clipboard with her as she moved through the hospital. She kept checking boxes off on a page she borrowed from a nurse's station as if she was inspecting the facility. Her cover wouldn't stand up to scrutiny if questioned, but nobody seemed to be interested in what she was doing. Stalling when needed, she made sure she got a good look at every medical worker in the hospital. Nobody seemed to match the old photo. She realized that Thach could have changed his appearance a great deal over the years. She found a work schedule and noticed that many doctors and nurses were not at work that day. She would need to come back later to look them over.

Cuong's cover was a truck driver looking for work in the area. While visiting various businesses, he dropped subtle hints that he blamed the current government for the decline in employment. He needed the communists to find him, not the other way around. He knew that they would be watching him. Whether they would be interested in recruiting him would be hard to determine. A truck driver was a common occupation. Nothing fancy but that's what Granier had wanted.

Understated. He didn't want Cuong to seem too eager to express his political views. It was a lot like fishing for salmon in a stream or river. Patience was required. Salmon scared easily and once they spotted danger; they were gone in a flash rarely returning.

It took a week of moving from town to town before he was finally contacted by a woman who suggested he attend a communist rally in front of a butcher shop just after dark. He said he would consider it but was concerned about the police. She said the police patrolling the area were communist sympathizers and would do nothing to interrupt the rally. Cuong said he did not want to be pressured into joining the communists. She insisted there would be no pressure. He could just listen and leave whenever he wanted. He agreed to go to the rally. Cuong had been reluctant just the right amount to cast off suspicions.

Informed of the rally, Granier gathered his team and developed an operational plan. The sniper unit would take up a rooftop surveillance position and provide covering fire if anyone in the team was in danger. They could also be used to eliminate Thach if he was found and could not be captured. The heavy weapons unit was divided, Rogers would provide a diversion if Thach was discovered, and the team was in a position to capture him. Cuong had made a flash-bang-type explosive device and instructed Rogers how to detonate it. Hammond became the team's driver and would wait in a hidden position with a car if Thach could be captured or if the team needed to escape. Sang and Cuong would participate in the rally while looking for Thach. Both would be armed with hidden pistols and knives. Granier would take a position where he could observe the team members and decide whether to capture or kill Thach if they found him.

The team would use newly developed, discreet hand signals to communicate. Granier made it clear that capturing Thach was preferred to killing him. He was part of a network that needed to be revealed and that would only happen with interrogation. Granier also didn't want Thach killed before he was sure they had the right man. It wasn't that Granier was overly concerned with assassinating a civilian. Collateral damage happened in war. He was concerned that the real Thach might escape. Granier did not find failure acceptable after being given an assignment. That was one of the big reasons he was selected to lead the team.

Thirty minutes before the rally was to begin, everyone took up their positions and spent their time surveying the area for any potential problems. The police were nowhere in sight as the woman that contacted Cuong had promised. Rally organizers set up a small platform on which the communist cadre could speak while being seen by all.

As people gathered, each was given a paper explaining the communist ideals and condemning the current government's actions. The communist cadre were very well organized. They kept an eye out for troublemakers that could be whisked off by the point of a knife without drawing attention. They wanted everything to run smoothly to prove to those attending that they were the right organization to run the country. It was small details that often made the difference in whether the crowd would convert in large numbers.

Just as the rally began and the first speaker stepped

up on the platform, Sang saw a familiar face among the various speakers standing by the platform. He was a doctor at one of the clinics. She had originally written him off because of his appearance. He looked nothing like the photo she was given. But on closer inspection, she saw that the distance between his eyes and the distance from the top of his upper lip and the base of his nose were similar to the photo. Those things could not be changed and stayed with a person their entire life. If it was Thach, he had done a good job changing his appearance. She looked down and saw that his shoes had been elevated to increase his height. Sang wasn't positive that it was him. She signaled Cuong to have a closer look at the man hoping he might be surer. He moved near the man and discreetly observed him. Cuong signaled back that he wasn't sure either.

Granier saw his two operatives observing the man. He used his binoculars to take a closer look. He too was unsure but felt there was a good possibility that the man was Thach. He didn't want him to escape.

When the first speaker was finished the man that looked like Thach stepped up on the platform and began to speak.

Granier could tell by the tone of his voice and his hand gestures that the man was an experienced and dynamic speaker. The crowd liked him and cheered as he spoke. Whoever he was, he was convincing the crowd that communism was the only future they should accept for their children and themselves. Granier decided to capture the man. He waited until the man was finished with his speech, then signaled the team. The rally ended with cadre moving through the crowd attempting to get people to join the Viet Cong or at least become communist sympathizers.

Sang and Cuong moved up closer to the man, one on either side of him. Rogers moved into position on the edge of the rally to the north and waited. Hammond started the car. As per Granier's hand signals, Fisher and York prepared to kill Thach with a sniper round if it looked like he was going to escape. The man that looked like Thach was surrounded by people congratulating him on his speech. Granier waited a few more minutes until the crowd thinned. It was the cadre still milling among the remains of the crowd that concerned him most. The Viet Cong were disciplined fighters and may not run off at the first sign of trouble. Granier would rely on the sniper team to take out any cadre that tried to prevent Thach's capture. It was time. Granier gave the signal for the capture operation to proceed.

Rogers detonated the flash-bang device near a trash bin. The explosion was harmless but loud and bright. It had the desired effect. The crowd ran in the opposite direction to the south. Sang and Cuong moved next to Thach who held his ground. Cuong pull out a knife and placed it in Thach's side and said, "Follow the woman."

Sang walked north toward the explosion and where the car was waiting. Thach and Cuong followed close behind Sang.

On the rooftop, Fisher manned the sniper rifle and kept the crosshairs on Thach's head. York used his range scope to survey the area and ensure that nobody was following. A nearby cadre approached Thach and told him he was going in the wrong direction. Rogers moved up and kneed the cadre in the groin. He fell to the ground moaning. Rogers fell in line behind Cuong as a rear guard. The cadre on the ground called out for help. Sang picked up the pace and the others followed.

They reached the car. Thach was pushed into the backseat with Rogers and Cuong on either side. Sang jumped into the passenger seat. Hammond threw the car in gear and took off. He didn't speed. He didn't draw any unwanted attention. Roger put a hood over Thach's head who kept saying he was a doctor that only wanted to help people and that they had the wrong man. Everyone ignored him. They find the truth of his identity shortly.

Granier, Fisher, and York used two motorbikes to make their way back to the warehouse. When they arrived, the man that looked like Thach was already tied to a chair in the room that had been prepared for interrogation. Sang had not begun. She waited for Granier's instructions although she already knew what he would say. "We need to know for sure that man is Thach or not. There can be no question," said Granier.

"There won't be," said Sang.

"Is there any way not to hurt him before we know if it really is him?"

"Do we have the time?"

"No. If it is him, the Viet Cong will be hunting for him."

"Then no. Quick is bloody."

"Alright. Get it done."

Sang moved off into the room and closed the door behind her. It was important that Thach see that she was not afraid to be alone with him, in fact, that was the way she preferred it.

The other team members waited in the warehouse and kept watch. They heard the first scream of the man being interrogated. It was unsettling.

Sang took her time. It was all part of destroying the

will of the subject. Two hours later, Sang emerged. Granier could see Thach through the open doorway. The tips of his fingers were bloody and missing their fingernails. They lay on the ground as if discarded. "It's him," said Sang.

"How sure are you?" said Granier.

"One hundred percent."

"Alright. Good. We need to know about the network. We need names."

"Alright. This next part will be crueler and messier."

"Okay. Do what needs to be done. Get the names."

Sang drank some tea and ate a few cookies before going back in. Granier was surprised by how easily he had ordered Thach tortured. He wanted to feel something more, but it just wasn't in him. Thach was a communist and recruited for the Viet Cong. He was the enemy. He convinced himself he would have felt different if Sang had said he was the wrong man. Granier trusted Sang. She knew her duty and did it without remorse or complaint.

Sang had been right. There was a lot more screaming and yelling. It was a nightmare to listen and stare at the closed door. None of the team wanted to go in there with her. Nobody wanted to witness the carnage.

Three hours later, Sang emerged from the room. Granier approached her and said, "Well?"

"He's done. If there was more to tell he would have already done it. It's a good list. Thirty-five names plus locations of a few weapon and ammunition stashes," said Sang.

"Alright. Good job."

"What do you want done with him?"

"You rest. I'll take care of him."

She moved off. Granier walked into the room. Thach was bloodied and cut. All his fingers were missing. There was a deep gash across his face and his eyes were swollen shut. Granier wasn't sure if she had removed them. Thach was trembling. He would never be the same again. He was beyond broken.

Even though he was in extreme pain, Thach knew by the heaviness of Granier's footfall that he wasn't the woman that had been torturing him. Thach had grown to recognize Sang's approaching footsteps as she moved from the table where she kept her tools to his side. The anticipation was almost more terrifying than the actual torture… almost. She was the master of the moment.

Granier heard a faint whimper. He moved closer and heard Thach say, "Kill me."

Granier considered for a moment. Bill would want Thach turned over to the South Vietnamese for further interrogation. Granier knew by looking at Thach that Sang was right. He had nothing more to tell. He didn't see the point of letting things go on and said, "Alright."

Granier removed his pistol from its holster. Thach could not see the gun, but he heard the chambering of the round, He smiled slightly before Granier shot him in the side of the head. He was dead. The pain and guilt were gone.

The next day, Granier went to the embassy in Saigon and sent Bill a coded message that said "Operation successful. Thirty-five names to add to your list. Three weapon stashes were identified. Target has been terminated."

Bill's response was almost immediate. He congratulated the team and their leader. He ordered three days for recovery before a new mission would be issued. It was all so understated considering the methods and results...

February 13, 1966 - Hanoi, North Vietnam

A specially outfitted Firebee 147E drone flew over the elephant grass-covered hills as it crossed over the North Vietnamese border on its way to Hanoi. The drone was on a one-way trip and was expected to be blown to smithereens by the North Vietnamese anti-aircraft units, hopefully by an SA-2 antiaircraft missile system. Inside the drone was electronic monitoring and radio equipment that would detect the signature from the SA-2 radar before being destroyed and transmit it to an American radio receiver. The idea was to get the North Vietnamese to attack the drone allowing the equipment inside to acquire the long-mysterious command uplink and downlink signals from the enemy radar. Once the Americans had the radar's precise signals they could develop an air-to-ground missile guidance system that would home in on the SA-2 systems when the North Vietnamese activated their radar.

As the Firebee flew over the countryside, an SA-2 radar picked it up. The drone broadcast the radar's signal data back to a nearby DC-130 that had been trailing the Firebee. The North Vietnamese team manning the system locked onto the drone and fired an anti-aircraft missile. A few moments later, the drone was blown to bits. It had served its purpose. Believing they had shot down an American fighter, the North Vietnamese cheered at the explosion and the fiery crash of the aircraft's wreckage. What they didn't know was that they had just given their enemy all they needed to defeat their most powerful weapon.

BATTLES OF NA KHANG

Houaphanh Province, Laos

There were few paved roads in Northern Laos, especially in the rugged mountains near the North Vietnamese border. Because of its northern location and proximity to the Special Forces camps in the area, the 500-yard compressed dirt airfield at Lima Site 36 was a vital supply base in the Laotian Civil War. The airstrip was capable of landing C-123 Provider cargo carriers but with little room to spare as there was a tall hill at the end of the runway. There was no chance of an aborted landing. The U.S. combat search and rescue Sikorsky helicopters nicknamed "Jolly Green Giants" were also stationed at the airfield.

The Hmong General Vang Pao saw the importance of the airfield and stationed several guerilla bases around Na Khang where Lima Site 34 and its airfield were located. Pao had five battalions of Hmong warriors and another 5,000 ADC militia troops in the region. In addition, 5,500 ADO home guards protected the villages. His Hmong warriors had been armed and trained by the American SOG teams. It was in their culture to fight bravely and often. The Americans made sure Hmong had plenty of ammunition to carry out their assaults on the communist NVA and Pathet Lao. While the Hmong wanted artillery, the SOG did not want them weighed down and kept them mobile. It was the one thing they denied the Hmong chiefs. As a conciliatory gesture, the SOG gave the tribes more mortars and recoilless rifles which were far more useful and portable in the mountains and jungles. The Hmong seemed satisfied for the moment. The SOG team members remembered when the hill tribes in South Vietnam rebelled against the ARVN officers and took several SOG teams hostage. Although the Americans were released unharmed, nobody wanted to anger the Hmong.

Na Khang was located next to Route 6, one of the key supply and transportation roads feeding into the Ho Chi Minh Trail. Military aircraft from the airfield continually harassed the communist convoys. The airfield at Lima Site 34 was a thorn in Hanoi's side and the politburo wanted it gone.

The leaders in Hanoi dispatched the 5th Battalion, 168th Regiment to assault Na Khang and capture the airfield. It took them almost a month to travel to Laos and position themselves for the attack. The commander of 5/168th had explicit instructions that he was to disregard casualties and overrun the airfield no matter the cost to the men under his command.

Just before midnight on the 16th of February, the NVA swiftly overran a Laotian outpost a little over a mile south of Na Khang. By sunrise, the NVA were shelling the town with mortars. A battery of Royal Laotian howitzers returned fire and drove the NVA back on a patch of high ground southeast of the town.

Having been notified of the attack, Tom Coyle flew the Black Widow, a specially modified AC-47 toward the enemy on the hillside. Once he spotted his prey, Coyle placed the gunship in a pylon turn at 2,000 feet. The crew readied the three miniguns as Coyle picked out his first target using the homemade site on the pilot-side window. The moment the gun crew announced the guns were up, Coyle squeezed the trigger. As always, there was the whirling of the six barrels on each of the miniguns wound up to speed, then the side-firing guns let loose sounding like a chainsaw gone wild. The guns firing reverberated off the walls of the aircraft's cargo hold with a deafening effect on the crew covering their ears as best they could.

Three red fingers of tracer bullet reached down from the aircraft in the early morning sky and tore the earth. Anyone in the bullet's path vanished in a red mist. It was frightening how efficient mankind had become at killing fellow humans. With artillery shells exploding sending shrapnel in all directions and the ungodly dragon in the sky, the NVA had nowhere to run and hugged the ground praying it would end.

The AC-47 could loiter for hours above the battlefield. But while it carried a large supply of ammunition, it also chewed through its supply of bullets like popcorn at a Saturday matinee. After only an hour, the gunship's ammo boxes were empty, and Coyle was forced to break off the attack and return to base to reload.

The NVA took full advantage of the reprieve and opened fire once again on Na Khang with their mortars. The Laotian howitzers continued to shell the enemy mortars, while the mortars shelled the town.

The U.S. Ambassador ordered Na Khang evacuated to nearby Lima Site 48 and sent in his Forward Air Controllers to direct close air support from seven sorties of F-105 fighters.

The NVA troops fought their way to the edge of the Laotian forces' defensive perimeter around the airfield. For the first time in Laos, Napalm was used to drive the enemy back. As the battle continued, General

Pao was wounded and medevacked by helicopter to Korat Royal Thai Air Force Base. With their courageous leader wounded, the Laotian morale sank like an anchor. A second drop of Napalm from the F-105s kept the NVA from destroying the Laotians protecting the airfield. Under the fiery cover, the Laotians withdrew from the site destroying any equipment left behind. The NVA would be left with nothing. Two more USAF AC-47 gunships arrived and opened fire on the enemy as they occupied the airfield.

There was little left of Na Khang or the airfield when the battle finished. The U.S. had bombed, napalmed, rocketed, and strafed the enemy with 165 sorties. The airfield runway had been cratered by 500 lb. bombs making it useless to the enemy. Even though the communists had captured the airfield as ordered, they had paid a terrible price with more than half their battalion wiped out and the Americans counted the battle as a victory.

The communists entrenched themselves around the airfield and built up their defenses with reinforcements. The first battle of Na Khang was over, and the communists had won. The second battle was about to begin.

After one-month, General Pao recovered from his wounds and resumed his duties. His soldiers were delighted to see their leader return and their morale returned to normal. Pao was determined to retake the airfield with his indigenous forces without the help of Royal Laotian Army regulars. He was tired of the Laotian military leaders believing that his warriors were second-class soldiers. He would prove them wrong.

In early May 1966, General Pao and his army

attacked Na Khang. U.S. Forward Air Controller Charles Jones directed American fighter airstrikes against the NVA forces. Air America helicopters ferried in more Hmong troops as the battle intensified. One of the helicopters was hit and crashed killing the pilot and nine Hmong soldiers.

Under a heavy barrage of artillery fire and air assaults, the communists were slowly forced to withdraw from Na Khang. As the NVA retreated, they were caught in the open by a flight of U.S. jets which inflicted numerous enemy casualties.

After one week of intense fighting, the Laotians were once again in control of Na Khang and the badly damaged airfield. The invading NVA force retreated all the way back to North Vietnam. But the fight for Na Khang was not over…

Over the next two years, there would be two more battles for Na Khang as NVA and Hmong fought for control of the airfield. In the end, it was the NVA that triumphed, and the airfield was shut down permanently until the end of the Laotian Civil War. Cargo and reinforcements on the Ho Chi Minh Trail increased dramatically since the nearby air threat had vanished.

The loss of Na Khang and the airfield at Lima Site 36 were a major blow to the South Vietnamese and American war effort as weapons and ammunition flowed into the south arming more and more Viet Cong.

February 17th, 1966 - United Nations, New York, USA

The member nations of the United Nations felt it was their responsibility to come up with a solution that would stop the wars in Southeast Asia. They believed that the policy of neutrality would bring about peace. The people of Southeast Asia should decide their fate through the ballot box.

Secretary-General U Thant developed a three-point proposal for ending the war and presented it through a spokesman to the U.N. assembly in New York. The proposal called for a cessation of bombing of North Vietnam, then a scaling down of all military activities, and finally, that all sides in the conflict, including the Viet Cong, would enter into negotiations.

The South Vietnamese refused to accept any negotiations with the Viet Cong, which they saw as insurrectionists and traitors to their country.

The Americans didn't like any idea that reduced the pressure they had been putting on North Vietnam. They also feared that any negotiations would eventually turn into a vote by all the Vietnamese people on the future of their country and who should rule. The Americans firmly believed that the South Vietnamese government would lose such a vote and thereby fall under the control of North Vietnam and the communists. Through their meddling, the U.N. would accomplish what the North Vietnamese and the Viet Cong had been unable to achieve through combat – the reunification of Vietnam and the expansion of communism. Once Vietnam was under communist control, the Americans believed it would not be long until Laos and Cambodia accepted communism for no other reason than to avoid war with their more powerful neighbors. The dominos would fall. Unlike the U.N. the Americans believed that South Vietnam had the right to determine its destiny without North Vietnam. The United States used its veto power to kill any resolution involving true democracy in a reunited Vietnam.

February 18, 1966 - Thua Thien Province, South Vietnam

Serving in Saigon at the 3rd Field Hospital in the Army Nurse Corps, Second Lieutenant Carol Drazba and Elizabeth Jones boarded a military helicopter at Tan Son Nhut Air Base along with seven other American military personnel. The helicopter lifted off without issue and headed out into the countryside.

After traveling a short distance, the helicopter developed mechanical problems and was forced to land. On its way to landing in a nearby field, the helicopter hit electrical lines and caught fire. The crew and passengers were unable to escape, and all died in the blaze.

Drazba and Jones were the first American military women to die in Vietnam. Six more female soldiers would die before the war was over. Their remains were returned to their families in the United States where they were buried with military honors.

March 9, 1966 – A Shau Valley, South Vietnam

Situated in the northernmost part of South Vietnam, the sparsely populated A Shau valley was a bottomland surrounded by steep mountainous terrain often cloaked by clouds and prone to abrupt changes in weather. Like much of Vietnam, it was beautiful but could prove to be deadly.

The U.S. Special Forces camp on the south end of the twenty-five-mile-long A Shau Valley was located just two and a half miles from the Laotian border and was the main outpost used to monitor the infiltration of NVA units into South Vietnam. The triangular-shaped fortress was surrounded by 200 yards of walls and had a barbed wire outer perimeter fence. The base's main lifeline was a 2,300-foot runway with a steel plank base just outside the perimeter capable of handling large transport and cargo planes. The strategically important base had originally been built in 1963 and quickly became a problem for the North Vietnamese traveling down the Ho Chi Minh Trail.

The camp was defended by ten Green Berets from the 5th Special Forces Group and 210 indigenous soldiers from the South Vietnamese Civilian Irregular Defense Group. In addition, nearby U.S. Air Commando units with A-1 Skyraiders and AC-47 Spooky gunships supported the camp's defenses. Since its inception, the camp had been relentlessly harassed by the NVA and Viet Cong.

On March 5th, two NVA defectors walked to the outskirts of the camp and surrendered. The camp commander was immediately suspicious but interrogated the soldiers anyway. The two defectors interrogated separately both disclosed that the NVA 325th Division had orders to assault the camp and destroy the forces therein. The defectors also gave the location of the 325th headquarters.

American air commandos flew reconnaissance flights over the location and detected a large buildup of troops and anti-aircraft emplacements. Airstrikes were called in. They bombed, Napalmed, and rocketed the NVA positions relentlessly for several days.

Even though the NVA commander knew that his forces had been discovered, he was not deterred from moving forward with his plans to attack the outpost with four of his battalions containing a total of 2,000 soldiers.

When the American Special Forces realized that they were going to be attacked by a superior force, the commander asked for reinforcements before the battle began. On March 7, seven additional Special Forces soldiers, nine interpreters, and a Mike Force Company arrived at the camp and took up positions within the perimeter walls. It was a tight fit. The Americans had packed in as many soldiers as the outpost could hold and they would still be outnumbered by 5 to 1. In anticipation of the attack, the American commander sent out night patrols to locate the enemy and provide some advanced warning.

On the night of March 8th, the NVA attacked. The NVA were initially beaten back by the allied forces and took heavy causalities. As the weather changed, American air power was hindered by a thick cloud cover. The NVA commander watched the weather deteriorate and decided to continue the assault.

In the early morning of March 9th, the NVA resumed their assault which began with an intense mortar bombardment of the Special Forces compound. In several places, the fortress walls were pounded into rubble creating dangerous breach points.

At 1 PM, an AC-47 Spooky from the 4th Air Commando Squadron was able to squeeze through the clouds and began circling the camp. Unable to achieve the 2,000-foot altitude it needed to fire down on the enemy, the aircraft was forced to fire its Gatling guns horizontally at the NVA formations assaulting the American perimeter. The NVA anti-aircraft weapons returned fire and shot down the slow-moving aircraft.

"Spooky 70" as it was called, crashed three miles north of the camp. Although several were wounded, all six of the crewmen survived the crash but were deep within enemy lines. The NVA attacked the downed aircraft almost immediately and killed three of the crewmen. The remaining three Americans destroyed the aircraft's three miniguns with grenades and smashed the gun system controls, then escaped into the surrounding jungle where they evaded the NVA patrols sent to capture or kill them. Eventually, a USAF Kaman HH-43 Huskie helicopter was able to reach the men and carried them to safety.

At 4:30 PM, a C-123 Provide and a CV-2 Caribou air-dropped ammunition and supplies to the besieged forces. The soldiers in the compound were disheartened when the parachutes landed outside the perimeter wire and could not be retrieved. Several brave helicopter crews flew into the camp and evacuated the seriously wounded while dropping off supplies and ammunition.

As the evening progressed the weather continued to deteriorate forcing the reinforcements being flown in by helicopter from Hue and Phu Bai to be called off. The camp's defenders were on their own. They repaired the breaches in the wall as best they could and hunkered down for the night. Most of the night, an AC-47 circled in the clouds above dropping powerful parachute flares that helped keep the enemy away.

Before sunrise on March 10th, the NVA attacked the fortress once again. At 5 AM, an NVA assault team penetrated the eastern perimeter. Hand-to-hand combat between the two sides occurred for several hours. The defenders fought well but were outnumbered and were forced to withdraw to the outpost's northern wall.

USMC and RVAF aircraft hit the NVA positions in and around the camp hard with rockets and bombs. During the air-to-ground assaults, an A-1 Skyraider was hit by a flurry of anti-aircraft fire as it dropped its bombs on an NVA position just outside the breached perimeter wall. The Skyraider's pilot, Major Dafford Wayne "Jump" Myers was unhurt, but his aircraft was badly damaged. His windshield was covered with oil, his cockpit was filled with smoke, and his plane was engulfed in flames.

Piloting an A-1 above the outpost, Major Bernard Fisher became the eyes of his friend Myers guiding him by radio to crash-land on the steel-plated runway. With little response from his controls and with Fisher's help over the radio, Myers was able to belly in his plane on the camp's airstrip. Only slightly wounded, he was only 200 yards from an enemy position firing on the camp when he climbed from the shattered cockpit and leapt from the burning wreckage. The black smoke obscured his movements from the nearby enemy. He crawled to an embankment paralleling the runway and took cover behind it.

Fisher could see that Myers was too close to the enemy and would not last the twenty minutes before a helicopter could rescue him. His friend would be killed or captured if nothing was done. A deeply religious Mormon that would not allow his friend to be killed or captured, Fisher acted. He ordered the other five Skyraiders in his group to keep the enemy away from Myers and give him cover as he attempted a rescue. Fisher was flying an A-1E with two seats. The other pilots gave their commander everything he asked for by hammering the enemy near Myers's crashed aircraft.

Fisher lined up his aircraft on the smoke-shrouded north end of the runway and landed on the steel-planked runway dodging craters and debris. Seeing the flames from Myers's burning aircraft approaching through the thick smoke, Fisher quickly realized that he wasn't going to make it and pulled up only moments before crashing into the wreckage.

Taking off again, Fisher banked his plane 180 degrees and approached the airstrip from the opposite end where there was more room to maneuver. He landed, slowed, then turned on the dirt at the edge of the runway, and taxied at full speed to the wreckage. Even with the cover provided by the Skyraiders above, Fisher's aircraft was hit multiple times by small arms fire. He caught a glimpse of Myers waving from the embankment.

Above, the gun and armament pylons of the Skyraiders providing cover were empty. Defenseless, they dove at the enemy anyway, hoping to keep their heads down and prevent them from firing on Fisher and Myers.

Questioning why his commander would take such a risk, Myers swiftly rose from the embankment and ran to Fisher's aircraft with enemy bullets bouncing off the ground and whizzing by his head. Within a minute, Myers was inside the Skyraider's cockpit and seated behind Fisher. "You dumb S.O.B. now neither of us will get out of here," said Myers.

"Have a little faith, brother," said Fisher.

They heard the plunks of enemy fire hitting the fuselage. Fisher wasted no time taking off and flying away from the battlefield. Fisher would be awarded the Medal of Honor by President Johnson for his actions. Myers would be forever grateful to his friend that risked his life to save him.

Even after 210 aircraft sorties, the Special Forces fortress in the A Shau was on the verge of falling to the enemy which kept up a relentless assault even after taking heavy losses. The Americans and their allies were running low on ammunition and had little hope of being resupplied before the weather lifted. The Special Forces soldiers had suffered a 100 percent casualty rate with five killed and twelve wounded but still fighting. The CIDG forces had over 250 killed and most of the survivors were wounded. Many of the civilians that had taken up refuge in the fortress had also been killed or wounded. MACV decided to evacuate the outpost their soldiers had fought so hard to defend. The Americans destroyed their communication equipment and all abandoned weapons and ammunition. They would leave nothing for the enemy.

Supported by four UH-1B gunships, fifteen H-34 helicopters airlifted the survivors making multiple trips. As the helicopters prepared to take off with the first batch of evacuees, the South Vietnamese soldiers, believing they were being left behind panicked, grabbed onto the helicopters, and forced their way inside preventing the overloaded aircraft from taking off. To unburden the helicopters, some of the Special Forces soldiers were forced to fire upon their allies until they disembarked allowing the helicopters to take off. Two of the transport helicopters were hit by enemy fire and crashed killing and wounding many onboard. Only 172 of the indigenous warriors were flown out. The rest were dead or escaped into the surrounding jungle.

At 5:45 in the evening, the camp was overrun by the communists and the fortress fell. The Americans had lost a vital asset in the war to keep the North Vietnamese from resupplying and reinforcing the Viet Cong and NVA. The communist forces turned the A Shau Valley into a heavily fortified position with anti-aircraft emplacements, artillery pits, and reinforced bunkers. From the A Shau, communist forces were able to stage attacks on Hue and other cities in Central Vietnam. The Americans and the South Vietnamese would launch multiple campaigns to retake the valley during the war. They were never able to hold the valley for more than a few weeks before the communists returned and reclaimed it.

DOPE

Central Mountains, Laos

The shadow of a Pilatus PC-6 Porter utility aircraft swept across the jungle-covered mountains. The Porter was easily recognizable because of its long snout holding its turboprop-powered engine. It was a STOL aircraft and tough which allowed it to land and take off in the most difficult locations.

In the aircraft pilot's seat, Coyle checked his map as he flew along the Chaine Annamitique, a long mountain range in central Laos. Looking out the side window he spotted a mountain peak taller than the rest and compared it to the landmarks on the map. He was on course as he headed for Xiangkhoang Plateau where he was scheduled to pick up several packages for Lucian Conein, his temporary boss who had a knack for getting whatever he wanted no matter who he had to blackmail. Coyle and his specially modified plane had been assigned to Conein through a contract with Air America. But Conein wanted Coyle for another reason: Coyle was a very good pilot and he owed Conein big time for helping save his girlfriend that ended up being killed anyway. Even though Bian had died a short time after being freed from captivity, Coyle had decided to honor the debt. He had given his word and while that mattered little to Conein, it mattered a great deal to Coyle.

As the plane approached the landing site on Xiangkhoang Plateau, Coyle decreased altitude. The landing site was nothing more than a dirt runway cut out of the jungle by the local Montagnard tribe. He set the aircraft down and turned the plane around at the end of the runway. The Montagnard tribesmen ran out onto the runway and loaded the plane with packages wrapped in brown wax paper. Inside each package were twenty-five kilos of raw opium. Coyle counted the packages to ensure they didn't overload the plane. The Montagnard were honest, but lousy at counting. They were also great warriors and fought against the Pathet Lao communists. Transporting their crops to market was part of the deal the SOG teams had made to enlist the Montagnard's help in the war in Laos.

In the beginning, Coyle was reluctant to transport opium. Opium wasn't illegal in Laos, but Coyle knew that most of what he carried would end up on the streets of Europe or America after it was processed into heroin. He had seen firsthand the lives heroin could destroy, especially with veterans returning from the wars trying to forget what happened. But he had also seen the good the money for the opium harvest could bring to the Montagnard tribesmen and their families. Opium was their only cash crop that provided medicine and tools for farming. They even built schools for their children with the money the drug provided.

Over time, Coyle had learned to be less judgmental and had accepted his role as a drug smuggler. Who was he to question a heroin user's decision? Still, he refused to transport the final product. He would only handle the raw brown tar and the money paid for it.

He had been flying for almost ten hours and felt tired. His thermos of coffee was long empty. He wanted to take a nap before taking off again, but it was getting late in the day and he still needed to fly to Vientiane, the capital of Laos to deliver the opium to the buyer, Major General Vang Pao, the commander of the Hmong Army making him an important American ally.

A medicine woman gave Coyle an herb to chew on that was supposed to help him stay awake. Coyle didn't want it at first, but he didn't want to insult the woman, so he put some in his shirt pocket. She insisted he try it. He popped a pinch in his mouth and chewed. It took effect immediately and he could feel his strength returning. He wondered what she had given him but decided that whatever it was it was better than falling asleep and crashing into a mountain.

Coyle climbed back into his plane and took off. The Montagnard watched him go. Even though he had their entire livelihood in the hold of his plane, they trusted Coyle and had faith he would return with their money and the supplies and medicine they had asked him to buy in the city.

The Pathet Lao had overrun the Plain of Jars which had airfields and was close to Long Tieng, the headquarters of General Vang Pao. Long Tieng was where the opium was processed into heroin. To solve the problem created by the loss of airfields when they were captured, Pao had an airstrip built in the middle of Long Tieng. The CIA which was supporting Pao and his Hmong army wasn't thrilled with the idea of the general being connected so closely with opium and heroin, but they continued to turn a blind eye to the general's major source of income beyond the aid that the Americans gave him. The entire process was becoming more efficient as the market for high-grade opium and heroin was growing. The Montagnard farmers grew opium in the mountains and the CIA transported the brown tar to Long Tieng. Business was good and Pao liked having the processing operations closer to his headquarters where he could protect his precious drugs until they were transported to foreign markets.

At times, Pao didn't need to send all his product to the west. Many of the American soldiers in South Vietnam had become addicted to heroin which provided a stable market just a few hundred miles away. It was a dirty little secret that the U.S. Military chose to ignore much of the time.

Coyle was thirty miles outside of Long Tieng when he observed a T-28D Trojan pull up next to him on his left side. The Trojan had all its insignia and identification removed. Two 20 mm cannon pods were mounted on its underwing hard points. The pilot was wearing a flight helmet with the reflective visor down. Coyle knew he was in trouble even before the Trojan pilot signaled for him to land. The Trojan was capable of speeds twice as fast as Coyle's Porter. The Porter had an M60 machine gun mounted in the cargo hold that could shoot outside the rear door when it was open. It was on the wrong side to engage the Trojan. Besides, the M60 was no match for the pair of autocannons. Even with his superior flying skills, in a dogfight, Coyle would most likely lose. He nodded to the Trojan pilot that he would comply.

As Coyle flew lower, he spotted a clearing in the jungle. It was the only place nearby where Coyle could land his plane, but he wondered what the plan was for the Trojan pilot. There was no way the warplane could land on the small clearing. Once Coyle was on the ground, he could easily escape into the trees and be safe from the aircraft's weapons, but he doubted it would be that easy.

The Trojan pilot gave him another signal to land. Coyle lined up his plane and hoped whoever cleared the field remembered to take out the big rocks and fill in the potholes. If not, he and the opium could end up in a fiery crash. He set the aircraft down without incident and rolled to a stop. Eight men wearing civilian clothes and carrying AK-47s emerged from the surrounding trees and moved toward the plane. Their faces were covered with baklava masks and their skin was covered with black grease paint. Coyle thought it was a good sign that they wanted to conceal their identities. It meant they probably wouldn't kill him. If they were going to kill him, why bother?

In the sky above, the Trojan circled like a vulture ready to swoop in and finish off Coyle if something went wrong.

One of the men opened the passenger door and stuck the barrel of his weapon just a few inches from Coyle's face. There would be no missing if Coyle tried anything. The AK-47s meant nothing as far as identifying the men. Such a weapon could easily be purchased at a local market along with enough ammunition to fight a small army. Coyle glanced at the man's eyes for a brief moment. They were light-colored and so were most of the eyes of the other men. They were American or European.

The packages of opium were quickly unloaded, and the men disappeared back into the jungle. Coyle looked up as the Trojan banked hard and disappeared over the trees.

Coyle was alive and grateful, but he wasn't sure how long that might last. He had lost the general's opium and knew he would be held responsible. He considered making a run for it but then decided to continue to Long Tieng. Running would do no good since the general had operatives everywhere including Saigon. Besides, his aircraft was almost out of fuel, and he would never make it back over the mountains without filling his tanks.

He turned his plane and took off from the clearing. He didn't have much time to think about what he would say once he landed. It was going to be awkward at best and deadly at worst. He would tell the truth about what happened because if he were caught lying, he was sure he would be killed in a gruesome manner. He hoped that his reputation as being reliable in the past would save his life and would remind General Pao that Lucien Conein had picked him for the assignment. Conein was well-known in the underground and had powerful friends including the head of the Corsican mob. Nobody wanted to go to war with the Corsicans. The Corsicans had a strong reputation of reaching the unreachable when they wanted revenge.

Long Tieng, Laos

As his plane touched down on the compacted dirt runway in Long Tieng, Coyle taxied to the buildings at the end of the runway. As usual, eight Montagnard warriors pointed their weapons at him and another eight pointed their guns at the surrounding area to protect the shipment from raiders. When his plane rolled to a stop, Coyle put his hands in the air to show his compliance. Several Montagnard rushed forward and opened the cargo door expecting to unload the bags of opium. They were disappointed and yelled at Coyle. Coyle didn't speak their language but understood their anger when one of the Montagnard hit him in the back of the head with the butt of his rifle. Things were off to a bad start.

Coyle watched as the Montagnard leader ran over to the U.S. advisor holding a satchel filled with cash that Coyle would return to the Montagnard in the mountains. The conversation between the two was brief. The advisor walked to the plane and said, "Where is it?"

"Stolen," said Coyle.

"You must have a death wish."

"It's the truth. An armed T-28 ordered me to set down in a clearing and masked men stole the cargo. There was nothing I could do."

"You could have died."

"I could have, but I'm not stupid."

"We'll see about that. Something tells me that General Pao will choose a slower form of death than a bullet."

"Okay, then… quit your blabbering and get on with it."

The advisor ordered the Montagnard to remove Coyle from the plane and load him into the back of a jeep. With two Montagnard guarding him and the advisor in the passenger seat, the jeep's driver took off, leaving the airfield.

General Pao was furious when Coyle offered his version of what happened. The advisor spoke quietly to Pao as if suggesting a course of action. Pao grunted his approval. The advisor turned to Coyle and said, "You have two days to return the opium to the general. If you fail, you die. If you run, you die. Dying will not be pleasant or short. You will suffer a great deal. Do you understand?"

"Yes. I understand," said Coyle.

The advisor said something to the Montagnard guarding Coyle. The Montagnard took out his long knife and slice through Coyle's shirt into his chest. Blood soaked his torn shirt. "A preview of things to come should you fail or run," said the advisor. "You may go."

Coyle was driven back to his plane and released. He wasted no time in taking off and heading for Thailand.

Nakhon Phanom Airbase, Thailand

Instead of flying back to South Vietnam, Coyle flew to Nakhon Phanom Airfield in Thailand which was less than two hours away from Long Tieng. He only had two days to figure something out and he didn't want to waste any time flying if it could be helped.

He went to the airbase's communication center and asked to be connected to U.S. Embassy in Saigon. When the operator came on the line, Coyle asked to speak to Lucien Conein. The operator said that Mr. Conein was not in at the moment and suggested he call back tomorrow. Coyle hung up. His mind was racing. He had to find Conein if he were to have any hope of living through the ordeal. Coyle wasn't sure that it wasn't Conein that had stolen the opium, but he didn't have anywhere else to turn. He considered where Conein might be at that moment and narrowed it down to three places – House of a Thousand Smiles which was his favorite whorehouse, the Intercontinental Hotel rooftop lounge, and Mathieu Franchini's restaurant headquarters of the Corsican mob.

He tried calling each and finally found Conein at Franchini's restaurant. He knew that Conein would be pissed off having his lunch with Franchini interrupted, but Coyle didn't care. When the receptionist said that Conein was unavailable, Coyle insisted that it was a matter of life and death that he talk to Conein. A few moments later, Conein came on the line and said, "It damned well better be life or death, Coyle."

"It is. Mine and maybe yours. The shipment got hijacked," said Coyle.

There was a long moment of silence, then Conein said, "We shouldn't talk on the phone."

"We've got no choice. The general has given me two days or else."

"That's pretty generous of him. He must like you. Tell me what happened."

Coyle retold the events of the hijacking as Conein listened, then said, "Did you recognize any of the hijackers?"

"No. I told you they were masked. Although, I did see that they weren't Asian."

"How's that?"

"Their eyes were light in color."

"Alright. Well, that's something. Did they behave like military or militia?"

"More military, I think. They were using AK-47s."

"That means nothing. I can buy an AK-47 at any

local market. Who met you at the airfield at Long Tieng?"

"A bunch of Montagnard and a U.S. Advisor with the payment in a satchel."

"Nathan Tanner?"

"I don't know. He wouldn't give me his name."

"It was Tanner. He's the only foreigner that Pao would trust with that much cash."

"Do you think he had something to do with the hijacking?"

"You mean besides planning and recruiting the hijackers?"

"Are you sure?"

"As sure as one can be about things like this. Tanner was a captain in the OSS and later became a U.S. Advisor when the CIA didn't offer him a job."

"So, what makes you think he would do something like this?"

"Tanner was assigned to General Pao about two years ago. Word was that Pao liked him but didn't trust his loyalty to the United States. Pao wanted him as his personal advisor and errand boy, so he started paying him under the table. I suspect it was a lot more than his military salary. Nothing creates loyalty like cash."

"So, why would he betray Pao?"

"An opportunity to make more money. That opium is worth a lot more than what Pao is paying the Montagnard. Once processed it could be worth hundreds of thousands, maybe a million. Tanner betrayed his country for money. I am guessing he would betray Pao for more money."

"But if Pao finds out, he'll kill him."

"I would imagine… and not in a nice way. But guys like Tanner don't worry too much about getting caught. They think they're smarter than everyone else."

"Is he… smarter?"

"He's no slouch… and ruthless which makes him even more dangerous."

"So, what do I do?"

"I would steal back the opium."

"You make it sound like it's simple. I don't even know how to find Tanner's team or the opium."

"Well, if you find one, you'll probably find the other. Look, you know how to find Tanner. He's gonna be with Pao. Kidnap Tanner, then torture him until he tells where the opium is located."

"Dammit, Conein. I'm a pilot, not special ops."

"What about your buddy Granier?"

"I don't know where he is. Some sort of special assignment."

"Well, you'd better make some new friends."

"That's it? That's your advice? Make new friends."

"I didn't say it was good advice."

"You got me into this mess, Conein."

"You got yourself into this mess, Coyle. You came to me for help when you lost track of your girlfriend and I obliged… at a price. I'm just calling in what is owed to me."

"I think you're looking at this the wrong way."

"How's that?"

"You vouched for me. If they kill me, you're next."

"Pao's not going to kill me. I set the whole transportation thing up."

"That's the past."

"He needs me."

"Are you sure about that?"

Coyle's question gave Conein pause. Coyle thought he could hear the wheels turning in Conein's head during the long silence. "Are you still there, Conein?" said Coyle.

"I am really getting tired of bailing you out, Coyle."

"Does that mean you're gonna help me?"

"It means I am thinking about it."

"Think quicker. There isn't much time."

"You're my slave after this."

"I already am."

"Fine. There is no time to send in a recon team, so you gotta do exactly as I say."

"I will. What if Tanner has already sold the opium and it has left the country?"

"No. He's smarter than that. He'd let things cool down before trying to move the opium. Pao would have his agents out looking for the stuff. Too much risk of being caught. It's hidden somewhere safe."

"That's good news."

"Maybe. It makes it harder to find if he's not moving it."

"Yeah, but he probably has it well guarded."

"Yes, he probably does. I'll know better when I get there."

"You're coming to Laos?"

"Like you said, it's my life too. I'm not going to put that in someone else's hands. The schedules gonna be tight, so don't fuck up. We won't get a second chance."

"When can you get into Laos?"

"Probably tomorrow about noon. I'll bring my team with me… and a present for General Pao to hopefully calm him down."

"Alright. What should I do?"

"Get back to Long Tieng so you can meet me when I'm done with Pao. In the meantime, you need to do some groundwork."

Following Conein's instructions, Coyle needed to get back to Long Tieng quickly. But he couldn't fly his plane back to the airfield without the opium. Pao would have him killed.

He made his way back to his plane and pulled out the maps he had taken with him. He scoured the maps and searched for another place to land near Long Tieng. He found several roads winding through the hills, but none look suitable for landing because of the curves. Most of the countryside was covered with rice paddies surrounded by earthen dikes creating an impossible landing setting. He did find a commercial dairy farm that he thought might work. There were hay and alfalfa fields surrounding the dairy. If he could figure out the direction of the furrows before landing it might work. But if he guessed wrong, he would tear his landing gear off and probably flip the plane. Unless the field was recently harvested or planted, the hay or alfalfa would cover the field making it hard to determine which direction he should land. To make matters more difficult, the dairy farm was at least fifteen miles from Long Tieng. He thought he might be able to find a ride on a truck or tractor. The dairy farm had a lot of cons and few pros, but it was the only place in the area that was even remotely suitable. He decided to attempt a landing there. The only silver lining that he saw was if he was killed in a crash, he no longer needed to worry about finding the opium.

Besides his service pistol, Coyle's only other weapon was the M60 mounted in the cargo area of the Porter. It was too big to carry around without being noticed. He would make do with his pistol – a SIG P210. When he joined the CIA, he was forced to stop using his Colt 1911. The way the CIA saw it, if captured, a foreign-made weapon could throw off the enemy into thinking the officer was from another country. It was ludicrous thinking, but the CIA was young. Firing a 9mm parabellum round, the SIG P210 was the closest, reliable weapon he could find to replace his Colt 1911. He carried two extra clips in his shoulder holster. It wasn't much if got in a firefight.

He considered waiting until tomorrow morning to fly to the dairy farm in Laos. It was getting late, and the sun was low on the horizon. A good night's rest would do him good. But he ignored his own reasoning and climbed into the Porter. He wanted to get the mission over with and took off with only an hour and a half of sunlight left.

Long Tieng, Laos

The sun had almost set when Coyle spotted the dairy farm. He was in luck. One of the alfalfa fields had just been harvested and he could see the direction of the furrows. That was where the good news ended. To land parallel to the furrows he would need to fight a varying crosswind. It wasn't ideal, especially since he was landing in a field, but it was all he had available, and decided not to whine about it. He would take his chances with the crosswind. At least he didn't need to worry about large rocks, he told himself.

He lined up the aircraft and descended cutting the power as much as he dared. The plane bucked when the crosswind increased in strength. He fought it, forcing the plane as best he could, trying to keep the wheels straight. The aircraft touched down in the field and immediately lurched to one side as the wheels found their paths between the furrows. The Porter rolled another fifty feet before coming to a stop near the edge of the field. Coyle gunned the engine and drove the plane out of the field and in front of the hay barn.

Hearing the plane's engine, the farmer emerged from his house and screamed at Coyle as he climbed out of the plane with a rucksack over his shoulder. Without saying a word, Coyle held up a wad of money. The farmer stopped screaming and smiled. Coyle motioned for him to help push the aircraft into his hay barn. The farmer complied. Coyle handed him the money after they closed the barn doors. Coyle pointed to Long Tieng on the map. The farmer pointed west. Coyle nodded his thanks and started walking as he folded up the map and slipped it into his back pant pocket.

Coyle walked for over an hour in the dark before a local villager with his water buffalo pulling his cart passed by. Coyle held up some more money and pointed to Long Tieng on the map. The villager nodded. Coyle handed him half the money and climbed on the back of the cart. The cart was full of hay. Coyle laid down and was asleep in less than two minutes.

Coyle woke to the sound of Laotian voices mixed with one of the cart's squeaky wheels. The cart had traveled all night and arrived on the outskirts of Long Tieng. The voices were from two farmers walking out to their fields in the early morning twilight. Coyle grabbed his rucksack and slipped off the back of the cart. He gave the villager leading the water buffalo the rest of the money. The villager was exhausted but happy. Coyle had paid him more money than he made in a month. He would sleep while the water buffalo grazed and rested before returning to his home. The Vietnamese were good at roughing it and could sleep almost anywhere as long as it wasn't raining.

Coyle moved off the road and into the surrounding jungle. He did not want to be seen by the guards that would surely man a roadblock at the edge of the town. He moved through the jungle until he could see the town. He pulled his binoculars from his rucksack and surveyed the area. There was a soft haze from dust and smoke over the houses and unpaved streets giving the town a dreamy appearance. Except for a few women stoking the morning fire to cook rice, the townspeople were still asleep. Coyle had no idea how he would find Tanner among the hundreds of homes and buildings. He needed to draw Tanner out in the open in order to locate him.

General Pao's home was easily recognizable. It was the largest house in town and had a formattable perimeter wall with armed guards patrolling. The general's compound had its own generator and fuel tank. Coyle considered for a moment... an attack on the general's compound would surely attract Tanner. It wouldn't be easy. There were four guards patrolling the compound – two inside the wall and two outside - and the sun would be up soon making any sabotage less feasible. He wasted little time thinking his plan through. He didn't have time. He moved toward the general's compound.

Coyle removed a lighter from his rucksack and hid the backpack in some bushes at the edge of a field next to the general's compound. The generator was silent and only used when the town's power went out. It was located in the back corner of the compound along with the fuel tank. Coyle approached the back of the compound wall and waited until the guard passed. With nobody in sight, he ran across a field next to the compound, climbed the wall, and lay flat on top of the wall. He watched as the guard inside the compound completed his route and walked around a corner of the house.

Coyle quietly jumped down. He moved to the generator's fuel tank and removed the cap on the filling spout. Looking around he spotted a wood pile used for the cooking fires. He moved to the pile and found a dried branch that had not been cut yet. He moved back to the fuel tank and placed one end of the branch down the spout soaking it with fuel. He pulled it back out and stuck the other end of the branch in the spout. He lit the top of the branch sticking out of the spout. It started to burn down. He moved back to the wall and climbed to the top.

Looking down he saw the guard had stopped to relieve himself a few feet away. Coyle glanced back at the burning branch and saw that it was close to the spout opening. He had little time before the fumes inside the tank would ignite. He was about to jump down back inside the compound when he saw the interior guard appear. The burning branch caught the guard's attention, and he rushed toward it. Coyle had no choice. He rolled off the top of the wall and landed outside of the wall next to the guard urinating in the bushes. Coyle withdrew his pistol from its holster and leveled it at the guard. Coyle motioned for the guard to surrender his rifle. He handed it over to Coyle. Coyle threw it over the wall into the compound and ran across the field as the fuel tank exploded sending a huge ball of flame into the morning sky.

Coyle grabbed his rucksack and moved into a group of houses. He changed direction and moved behind a stack of bamboo where he could see the front of the compound and stay hidden. Having heard the explosion, villagers, some armed with rifles, were running down the street toward the general's compound. Thirty soldiers from the nearby barracks also arrived carrying rifles.

Three minutes later, Tanner appeared running toward the compound from the opposite direction. He looked disheveled as if he had thrown on his clothes and boots. Barking out orders to soldiers that had arrived, he buttoned up his shirt and disappeared inside the compound. The soldiers moved off in groups of three to search the surrounding area. Coyle covered himself with bamboo poles as the soldiers passed. He stayed hidden and kept observing the compound. He looked down at his watch. Conein and his team would be arriving soon. He needed to be ready. He knew he could only push Conein so far.

It was almost thirty minutes before Tanner emerged from the compound. Coyle could see that he was angry and barking out more orders to anyone standing around with a rifle. He wanted the saboteur found. Tanner walked down the street in the opposite direction. Coyle needed to follow him but there were still a good number of soldiers searching houses in the area. At that point, getting caught would most likely mean death. Even so, he had to risk it.

He moved to the opposite side of the main street and climbed into an animal pen and moved between two houses to an alley in the back. The alley looked empty. He moved down it quickly paralleling Tanner's path. He ducked into cover whenever somebody appeared. After two minutes, he caught up with Tanner still walking down the main street. Coyle followed him and watched as he entered a small building with a radio antenna on the roof. Coyle moved up to a window and peered inside the building. There was a Laotian soldier operating the radio with Tanner standing behind him giving instructions.

Coyle heard the sound of a plane engine in the distance. He looked into the sky and saw a Porter coming in for a landing on the airfield. He surmised it was Conein and his team. Coyle was out of time.

Coyle pulled out his pistol and burst into the communications building. Tanner reached for his sidearm. Coyle charged forward and pistol-whipped Tanner on the side of the head, knocking him out cold or killing him. Coyle wasn't sure. He went down in a lump and wasn't moving. The Laotian radio operator reached for his rifle. Coyle pointed his weapon at the man's head. He released his rifle and put his hands in the air. Coyle removed the plastic-coated wire and a pair of wire cutters from his rucksack and used them to tie the hands of the operator and Tanner. Coyle could see that Tanner was breathing. He was relieved. He pushed the operator into a closet, closed the door, and shoved a chair up against the doorknob. He could see that Tanner was starting to come around.

Coyle sat in front of the radio and turned the frequency dial to the number Conein had given him. He called Conein on the plane's radio. When Conein answered, Coyle told him where he was and that he had received the package they had discussed. Conein responded that he would be there in an hour or so and to keep the package safe. Coyle turned the frequency to another channel.

A few minutes later, Tanner regained consciousness. His head was bleeding but not badly. "You really do have a death wish?" said Tanner seeing Coyle.

"You shouldn't have reached for your gun," said Coyle.

"Instinct."

"I guess I could see that."

"What's your plan?"

"We wait."

"For what?"

"For whom. In the meantime, shut up or I'll use you like a punching bag."

"Big talk from a man that..."

Coyle walked over and kicked him in the stomach before he could finish his sentence. "You really should listen better," said Coyle sitting back down.

An hour later, Conein and three armed Corsicans showed up. The Corsicans carried Beretta 38-A submachine guns, reliable relics from WWII while Conein carried a Carl Gustaf M/45 with a folding stock and brought an extra for Coyle. "How'd it go with Pao?" said Coyle.

"I'm here, ain't I?" said Conein handing Coyle the spare submachine gun.

"What are doing here, Conein?" said Tanner.

"Doing what I should have done a long time ago, you piece of shit."

"I don't know what you're talking about?"

"I'd bet dollars to donuts you know exactly what I'm talking about, Tanner."

"General Pao's gonna feed your balls to his dog if

you don't let me go right now."

"General Pao is too busy playing with the pair of French dueling pistols I just gave him to worry about you. You know how he likes nice things."

Conein said something to the Corsicans. They pick up Tanner and put him in a chair. They removed his belt and lashed his feet to the chair so he couldn't kick or escape. Two of the Corsicans removed their belts and connected them using their buckles, then wrapped them around Tanner's torso lashing him to the chair with his hands still tied behind his back. Conein pulled a box from his rucksack and opened it. Inside, were dental tools. "What are going to do with those, Conein?"

"Dig out the truth."

"Jesus."

"He ain't gonna help you."

Conein looked around the room, then walked over to the door, picked up a wooden doorstop, and said, "That should do nicely."

He walked back over to Tanner and said, "Open your mouth."

"Wait. You haven't asked me anything," said Tanner.

"I don't need to ask you anything. You know what I want to know."

"No. I don't."

"Open your damned mouth, Tanner."

Tanner clamped his mouth shut. "Have it your way," said Conein pulling out his combat knife and moving toward Tanner's closed mouth.

Tanner's eyes went wide, and his mouth shot open before the knife's blade reached his lips. "Now you're getting the idea," said Conein shoving the wooden doorstop into one side of Tanner's mouth to keep it pried open. "I think I'm gonna need a little more light."

One of the Corsicans pulled Tanner's head back and held it. "Now, let's see if you have been brushing your teeth regularly," said Conein as he selected a dental pick and began probing Tanner's teeth for cavities.

It didn't take long for him to find one and dug into it with his probe. Every muscle in Tanner's body went tense like he was being electrocuted. He screamed. "Oh, I think I found one," said Conein.

As Conein continue to probe the cavity, Tanner whimpered. "The problem with teeth and cavities is that after a while, the patient will stop feeling pain as the nerves recede. Of course, it takes a while. And the dentist can always move on to the next cavity, then circle back around once the nerve endings have had a rest," said Conein.

Tears streamed down Tanner's face as he tried to say something. "I'm sorry. I can't understand you with that wooden wedge in your mouth. Give me a minute and I'll take it out," said Conein as he continued to probe the cavity. Tanner sounded like he was pleading. "Okay. Okay. I hear you. But just so we are clear... I am only going to take the wedge out for fifteen seconds, then it goes back in, and I continue. You might want to think deeply about what you want to say."

Conein set his dental pick down and tried to pull out the wedge. Tanner's teeth had dug into it, and it wasn't moving. "I was afraid of that," said Conein. "I'm gonna need a little help."

A Corsican put both his hands inside Tanner's mouth prying open his mouth. The wooden wedge came loose and Conein pulled it out, then said, "You have something you wanted to say."

"It's at a SOG outpost near the clearing where the plane landed," said Tanner.

"What is?" said Conein.

"The opium that my men stole."

"You mean that you stole."

"Yes. The opium that I stole."

"Winner, winner, chicken dinner. You'll be going with us, and I'll be bringing my dental tools and the doorstop along, just in case. Do you understand?"

Tanner nodded anxiously.

The porter took off with Coyle in the pilot's seat, Conein, Tanner, and the three Corsicans. Thirty minutes later, Coyle set the plane down in the clearing. The Corsicans jumped out first and set up a defensive perimeter. They were Franchini's bodyguards and knew how to protect their boss. Carrying their submachine guns, Conein and Coyle climbed out and pulled out Tanner, his hands still tied. "I have no problem shooting you in the back if you run, Tanner. Things are easily lost in the jungle, and nobody ever finds them," said Conein.

"You're gonna kill me anyway once you have the opium," said Tanner.

"No. I'm not. In spite of being an asshole and a traitor, you're still an American. I don't kill Americans. That's a line I won't cross. Are there any boobytraps from here to the SOG outpost?"

"A few."

"Good. We'll follow you."

"I should radio them."

"I don't think so."

"If walk into the outpost unannounced they could open fire thinking we're Pathet Lao."

"We'll take our chances. Now move."

Tanner led the way into the jungle followed by Conein and Coyle. The Corsicans watched the flanks and the rear.

After an hour of hiking through the jungle and circumventing three boobytraps, Tanner stopped and said, "It's just over that next knoll. We need to let them know we're coming in."

"I have a better idea," said Conein taking his rucksack off his back. He opened his rucksack and pulled out a satchel charge plus several grenades. The Corsicans did the same with their rucksacks. "Isn't that a little overkill?" said Coyle.

"Their SOG, Coyle. There isn't such a thing as overkill."

"You're not going to give them a chance to surrender?" said Coyle.

"They're not going to surrender. They've crossed the line. There is no going back."

"You said you don't kill Americans."

"Except when they try to kill me."

"Well, they haven't done that."

"Look. You wanna march in there and ask nicely for the opium they stole from you; you go right ahead."

"I didn't say that. I just think they should be given a chance to surrender."

"Nope. Not gonna happen."

"What if you blow up the opium?"

"There is always that chance."

"Shit, Conein."

"Yeah, it's a real mess, ain't it?"

"Let me take Tanner and try to get them to

surrender."

"That's a mistake, Coyle. They're gonna kill you."

"Yeah, well… I'm hard to kill."

Conein laughed and said, "No. You're really not."

"I've seen enough men die for stupid reasons."

"That's a crock of shit. But if you wanna give it try, go ahead."

"Thanks. One last thing… if they do kill me…"

"Yeah, yeah. I'll kill them."

"Thanks."

Coyle pointed his assault rifle at Tanner and said, "One wrong move and I swear to God, I'll empty a clip into you."

Tanner nodded, more hopeful. Conein ordered the Corsicans to get into position. They split up and disappeared into the jungle. Conein turned to Coyle and said, "If things go south, and I am betting they will, get as low as possible and keep your head down. We filled those satchel charges with nails."

"Alright," said Coyle.

"Good luck, you fool," said Conein disappearing into the jungle.

Coyle ordered Tanner forward and kept the barrel of his submachine gun pointed at Tanner's back as he followed him.

As they approached the crest of the hill, Coyle saw the outpost below. A chest-high wall of sharpened, wooden stakes formed the outside perimeter. There was a three-foot-high earthen mound that formed the inner perimeter of the outpost. A light machine emplacement on a wooden tower with a 360-degree field of fire supported the entire camp and was manned by two Americans. Two more Americans stood in a mortar pit in the center of the compound. "Alright, Tanner. Call your men and let them know we're coming in," said Coyle.

Tanner called into the camp. The team leader, Jason Bell, flanked by two SOG soldiers, appeared at the main entrance and waved them in.

"You keep your mouth shut, Tanner," said Coyle as they approached the entrance.

"Of course. You're the boss, Coyle," said Tanner.

"What are you doing here, Tanner? The deal was you stay away," said Bell.

"He didn't have a choice in the matter," said Coyle.

"I can see that. You're the pilot of the Porter."

"Yep."

"Are you alone?"

"Nope."

Bell looked around, saw no one in sight, and said, "I'll take your word for it. What do you want?"

"The opium you stole."

"Or what?"

"Or my team is going to kill you."

Bell laughed and said, "They must be some real badasses."

"They are."

"Are you sure you have enough to take us? We're dug in like a tick."

"We have enough."

"I wonder."

"Give me the opium and you can have Tanner."

"What if I don't want him?"

"Knock it off, Bell," said Tanner. "I set this thing up and planned everything."

"You sure did. Thank you."

"What's that supposed to mean?"

Bell leveled his submachine gun and squeezed the trigger. Tanner was riddled with bullets. Coyle dove behind an ant hill. Tanner fell dead. Bell and his two guards opened fire on the ant hill tearing it apart. Coyle put his submachine gun over the top of the ant hill and opened fire without aim or even looking. It was strangely effective. Bell and the two soldiers stopped firing and dove behind the earthen wall.

The machine gun in the tower opened fire on Coyle. It was a hopeless situation as he watched his cover dissolve into clumps of hardened soil. He heard the thud of a mortar shell being launched. Moments later, the shell exploded twenty feet away from his feet. Even though he wasn't hurt, he knew it wouldn't take them long to adjust their fire and land a shell right on top of him. He was gonna die. The faces of his children flashed before his eyes. They would survive him. That was a good thing.

One of the Corsicans opened fire with his submachine gun from the edge of the jungle while a second Corsican ran forward firing his weapon in one hand and carrying a smoking satchel charge in the other hand. When he reached the outer perimeter, he dropped his gun and used both his hands to launch the satchel charge over the wooden stakes and the earth wall. It landed inside the outpost. The explosion was massive and shook the ground. Flying nails peppered two of the SOG soldiers. Both fell badly wounded, unable to continue the fight.

Another mortar shell exploded just five feet from Coyle. Pelted with rocks and dirt clouds, he was surprised he wasn't dead. The last of his ant hill was shaken to pieces by the explosion. Coyle crawled through the grass into the small crater where the second mortar shell had exploded. It wasn't much, but it was all he could find at the moment. He reloaded his weapon, aimed, and fired at the outpost.

Next came Conein with that third Corsican firing his submachine gun. Conein ran with the smoking satchel with his submachine gun still over his back. As he approached the wooden stake wall, he swung the satchel around several times like a hammer thrower. When he released it, it easily cleared the earthen wall and landed in the center of the outpost next to a stack of mortar shells. The initial explosion killed the two-man mortar crew and destroyed the mortar tube. The secondary explosions took out one of the legs of the machine gun tower. The tower fell. The two-man machine-gun team jumped to what they thought was safety just before the tower landed. A pole from the tower's roof impaled the shoulder of one of the men. He lived for a minute before dying of shock.

Satchel charges from the two Corsicans landed in the outpost just moments apart, exploding one after another. Nails flew in both directions shredding two more soldiers. Nowhere was safe.

During the confusion, Coyle rose and joined Conein and the Corsicans as they stormed the outpost firing their weapons and throwing grenades.

The surviving SOG soldiers had watched half their team get killed in less than three minutes. They had had enough and retreated out the back of the outpost, disappearing into the jungle. Bell fired his weapon one last time, then ran to the mess hut. He knocked over several stacks of rations to reveal a group of baskets filled with bags of opium. He pulled out two bags and ran for the back of the outpost. A Corsican stepped out from behind a tent directly in Bell's path. Bell yelled and kept going. The Corsican stepped aside to let Bell pass but held out his straight razor allowing Bell's neck to be sliced as he ran past. Bell kept going, carrying the bags of opium while trying to stop the bleeding from his neck. It didn't work. An artery in his neck had been cut and was pumping out his life's blood. He stumbled and dropped the bags of opium. He fell a few yards past the back of the outpost. He bled out a minute later and died.

The Corsicans ran into the jungle to hunt down the remaining SOG members. "Should we follow them?" said Coyle.

"Nah. Let them have their fun," said Conein.

"We just wiped out a SOG outpost. What are we going to tell MACV?"

"We're not going to tell them anything. When they find them, they'll just assume the Pathet Lao did it."

"And what about General Pao?"

"As long as he gets his opium back, he's not going to say or do anything. That's one thing about the general... the man has his priorities straight."

"Thanks for your help, Conein. You saved my ass."

"Don't worry, Coyle. I'll just put it on your tab."

THE STRUGGLE

March 26, 1966 – Hue, South Vietnam

The Perfume River, always jade green and moving at its own pace, flowed quietly past the Imperial Citadel, former home to the Nguyen Lords and Kings. The fortress was surrounded by a high stone wall. Inside the walls were lush gardens, sculpted shrines, and beautiful villas for the mandarin scholars that ruled the country with their abacuses and ledgers. Hue had been the capital of Vietnam for over 400 years until the French took over their colony and moved the capital to Hanoi. Even with the bureaucrats gone, Hue remained the heart of Buddhism in Vietnam.

For most of Vietnam's history, the government rulers and Buddhists worked and lived in harmony. It wasn't until western countries interfered with the government that the trouble started. President Diem had been a member of the Catholic Vietnamese minority. Unlike most Catholics, Diem was not afraid to make waves in favor of the church and its congregation. The Catholic church was given tax concessions and became the largest landowner in all of

Vietnam. Military promotions and public service positions were given to the faithful Catholics while the Buddhists were shunned and even punished for refusing to convert. Some Buddhist villages converted en masse to continue receiving aid and to avoid being forcibly resettled in fortified hamlets.

The French had given the Buddhists the official status of "Private" which required them to secure official permission whenever they wanted to conduct Buddhist activities in public. The status also allowed the government to greatly restrict the construction of Buddhist temples. The private status of the Buddhists was continued by the new government after the French were defeated and left the country. The double-tiered, biased status enraged the Buddhist leaders, especially Thich Tri Quang, a popular activist monk in Hue.

After the assassination of President Diem and his notorious brother Nhu, the Buddhist leaders thought things would change. They didn't. Much of the bias against the Buddhists continued. The Buddhists were seen as troublemakers by many of the military junta leaders that took over the government in a coup. No opposition against their rule was allowed by the leaders of the junta. The Buddhists rebelled and so began the "Struggle Movement."

The series of coups that plagued the military junta as they attempted to take tighter control of the reins of power, encouraged the Buddhist leaders who kept up the pressure for reform. General Nguyen Van Thieu and Air Marshal Nguyen Cao Ky finally established a stabilized government with Thieu as the figurehead of state and Ky as Prime Minister. In fact, South Vietnam had become a feudal system where an alliance of warlords ruled their respective areas of control while collecting taxes and handing over what they wished to Saigon keeping the rest for themselves. It was authorized corruption. The Buddhists were the warlords' harshest critics. The tension increased between the Catholic factions that wanted to protect the advantages they had gained over time and the Buddhist factions that wanted reform and justice. The Buddhists outnumbered the Catholics 10 to 1, but it was mostly the Catholics that sat in the government and military chairs of power.

General Nguyen Chanh Thi was the commander of I Corps which was assigned to protect the five provinces in and around Hue and Da Nang. Thi had two divisions under his command and was known to garner deep loyalty from his troops. Thi was a Buddhist and, being sympathetic to the Buddhists' grievances, enjoyed the support of the Buddhist leaders and the community in the area including the regional militia and popular forces. As time moved on and his power base grew, Thi became more belligerent against the government and at times, refused Ky's orders. Thi allowed students to publish a magazine that was highly critical of the government and the military junta. Thi had one of his trusted subordinates assigned as the commander of the national police which increased his political power.

Ky and other members of the ruling junta saw Thi as a legitimate threat. Some believed Thi might even attempt to succeed from both North and South Vietnam turning Central Vietnam into an independent state.

In February 1966, Ky flew to Honolulu, Hawaii to attend a summit. During the meeting, Ky said that Thi was a born intriguer and had left-wing inclinations.

Many believed that Thi had a greater following than Ky and that Thi could seize power anytime he wished. Because of Thi's neutralist stance, the Americans grew concerned. They didn't want anyone in the government to negotiate peace with the North Vietnamese communists. It was during that time that Ky became convinced the Americans would support his move against Thi.

Shortly after returning to Saigon, Ky mustered the support of eight of the generals in the ruling junta. With the junta's support, Ky decided to move against Thi and had him taken into custody after removing him from command of the I Corps. Ky informed Thi that he would be sent to the United States to receive medical treatment for his nasal passages. Ky accused Thi's mistress of being a communist and Thi of ruling his territory like a left-wing warlord. The junta-appointed Thi's subordinate General Nguyen Van Chuan as the new commander of I Corps.

Upon hearing of Thi's removal and pending exportation, Thich Tri Quang organized large Buddhist protests and demanded civilian rule of the government. Thi's dismissal caused widespread demonstrations throughout Central Vietnam and even in Saigon. A general strike in Da Nang, the second largest city in South Vietnam brought the city's businesses and local government to their knees.

By mid-March, Ky still had not expelled Thi who was under house arrest. Ky wanted to dampen the Buddhist discontent first before making such a bold move. He met with Buddhist leaders and promised new elections and social reform. His promises carried little weight and the demonstrations continued. As a final move to restore order and as a goodwill gesture,

Ky agreed to allow Thi a final visit to Da Nang and Hue, his old area of command, before departing the country.

While waiting for a new embed assignment, Karen went to Da Nang to photograph the expected demonstrations when Thi arrived. She was surprised when 20,000 students and supporters showed up to greet Thi. Thi was surrounded and swept away from his government guards by the mob. Karen did what she could to capture the moment with her camera. She was shoved from side to side as the cheering protestors surged forward.

The protestors took over the radio station in Da Nang and broadcast anti-junta propaganda. Ky did not want to risk escalation by retaking the radio station, so he chose to ignore the broadcasts, but the demonstrations continued and grew in number as word spread. The protests swelled to over 10,000 demonstrators and some became violent smashing windows in buildings and setting tires on fire in the streets filling the sky with black smoke. The police were vastly outnumbered and not anxious to intervene with the belligerent protestors.

Because of the anti-American rhetoric, Karen was concerned about going out on the street to cover the protests. She wondered if the student and protestors would respect her press credentials as a neutral party. She was safe in her hotel where armed security guards protected the guests. But she knew she couldn't cover the protests from the hotel lobby. She mustered her courage, grabbed her camera, and went out onto the street.

She found a large mob of students moving down a nearby boulevard. Taking a deep breath, she moved to the front of the students and started snapping photos. She was relieved when the students didn't attack her. They all wanted their pictures taken even though their faces were covered with plastic bags and cloth bandanas. Karen was more than happy to oblige and pretended to keep snapping photos when she ran out of film. Her camera kept her safe.

A short time later, protestors and students took over the radio station in Hue and began broadcasting their propaganda against the government and the military junta. Strangely, the students who criticized the Americans for supporting the South Vietnamese government, played "The Stars and Stripes Forever" during breaks between speeches. Americans were democratic and the South Vietnamese wondered why they supported the military junta that ruled their country. It was confusing and often tore at the protestors' loyalties, especially the students. On the one hand, they admired the Americans and their culture, and on the other, they despised the Americans for helping their adversaries and supporting a corrupt regime.

By the end of March, most of I Corps was operating independently from Central Vietnamese control. Even the Mayor of Da Nang openly supported the soldiers in rebellion against the government and refused to obey Ky's orders to get the mob under control. The Americans became more concerned and told Ky he must act to regain control of the military or risk losing the portion of U.S. aid going to I Corps.

Ky responded by firing the police chief of Hue, a Thi loyalist. The local police retaliated by going on strike and demonstrating against the chief's removal. Within days, 20,000 protestors, some military personnel in uniform, marched in the streets of the imperial capital of Hue. A general strike was called and the operations at the Da Nang Port came to a standstill. Protestors were demanding that Ky, Thieu, and Co be executed in public for their misdeeds and betrayal of the people. The protestors also demanded that the Americans stop interfering with politics or be kicked out of the country.

Ky sent General Pham Xuan Chieu to talk some sense into Thi and rally him to the side of the military junta. When Chieu arrived in Hue, he was surrounded by a group of students and was abducted. The students loaded him up in a cyclo and drove him around the city to show the people their prize before they released him unharmed. He returned to Saigon without meeting with Thi and informed Ky that Hue was overrun by protesting students and out of control.

At the beginning of April, Ky held a press conference where he claimed that Da Nang was under the control of the communists. He vowed to reclaim the city no matter the cost and kill the traitorous Mayor of Da Nang.

The next evening, Ky deployed three battalions of Marines to Da Nang using U.S. military aircraft. The Marines waited at Da Nang Air Base until they were joined by two battalions of Vietnamese Rangers plus riot police and paratroopers. It was an impressive show of force.

Karen knew a Marine aviator at Da Nang Air Base whom she had met while he was on leave in Saigon. They shared some time together until he had to return to Da Nang. He flew a Phantom F-4B fighter-bomber. When she heard about the South Vietnamese loyalist troops arriving in Da Nang, she decided to cover the story. The problem was that Air Marshal Ky had shut down the air base to visitors. She called the Marine aviator and asked if he wanted to have lunch. He said he couldn't leave the base at the moment. She suggested that she go to the base and meet him. He agreed to try and get her in under the guise of her doing a story on his squadron. It worked and the next day, Karen was allowed on the air base.

While riding in a jeep to the Marine compound, she snapped photos of the South Vietnamese troops marching in formation on the tarmac and newly made machine-gun emplacements around their ARVN barracks. She also took photos of the South Vietnamese aircraft undergoing last-minute maintenance. It seemed the ARVN and VNAF were preparing for battle. Her photography in the moving jeep wasn't great, but she was the only photojournalist on the air base at the time of Ky's military buildup.

Instead of leaving the base after having lunch with the Marine pilot in the officer's club, Karen unofficially embedded herself and found an empty bed in the nurses' barracks by the base hospital. She became friends with some of the Marine field commanders so she could hitch rides on transport aircraft when the Marines were deployed outside the base. She got to know the American guards, so they recognized her and didn't ask a lot of questions. It was a good setup for her and gave her access to more missions while she continued to cover the story of Ky's royalist troops against the rebel troops in Da Nang and Hue.

Ky flew to Da Nang to personally take over the operation and intimidate the protestors and the rebel ARVN soldiers into submission. Ky's appearance in Da Nang had the opposite effect as more civilians and rebel soldiers joined the Struggle Movement. Things became serious as the two South Vietnamese military forces hurled threats and prepared to do battle against each other.

General Chuan, the commander of I Corps, deployed his forces to block all routes in or out of the Da Nang Air Base. He then informed Ky that his forces within the Air Base would not be allowed to leave and that any attempt to do so would bring violence. Chuan told Ky that political issues should not be solved by the military. A short time later, General Nhuan, the commander of the 1st Division came out in support of the Struggle Movement and told Ky he and his men would fight Ky loyalists if they tried to enter the city of Hue.

Facing two divisions and what would surely become a bloodbath, Ky backed down and ordered his forces to stand down. It was a huge embarrassment for the prime minister as he flew back to Saigon having accomplished nothing. The protests around the country grew even more with tens of thousands of civilians taking part. The demonstrations in Saigon were the most violent where students used bicycle chains and sticks as weapons against the police. They threw rocks at passing cars and smashed the windows of businesses while chanting anti-American slogans.

The police used tear gas and sometimes hand grenades to disperse the protestors who fought back with rocks, homemade spears, and glass bottles. The students picked up the smoking tear gas canisters and hurled them back at the police. When a grenade was thrown by the police, the protestors fled the area until the grenade exploded. Undeterred, they returned to confront the police becoming even more violent.

The Buddhists called for a new constitution and for the junta to hand over power to elected civilians. The Buddhists also wanted amnesty for participants in the riots and the rebel soldiers. But even the Buddhists were not of one mind and argued among themselves about what should and should not be included in the constitution. Riots broke out in the Central Highland towns of Ban Me Thuot, Da Lat, and Pleiku. Buddhist monks staged sit-down protests at government buildings, main roads, and radio stations until the police dispersed them with clubs.

General Lewis Walt, the commander of U.S. forces in Da Nang found himself caught between two opposing South Vietnamese military factions. The Americans needed all the South Vietnamese soldiers they could get to fight the Viet Cong and NVA, and here were two South Vietnamese forces about to annihilate each other. Walt, with MACV's permission, ordered non-essential U.S. Military personnel, American civilians, and foreign nationals to be evacuated from Da Nang. American helicopters and landing craft transported over 700 evacuees to the Tiensha Peninsula out of harm's way.

Karen was told to evacuate. She refused and acknowledged she was putting herself in harm's way and that the Marines might not be able to protect her. It was a hot story, and she wasn't about to give it up just because things were getting a bit dicey.

Stationed in Hoi An, ARVN Colonel Dam Quang Yeu was pro-Struggle Movement. On April 9, 1966, Yeu ordered his battalion in Hoi An to proceed to Da Nang where they would engage government troops from Saigon. Yeu's convoy included armored personnel carriers, tanks, and artillery.

Walt decided to weigh in with the U.S. Marines in hopes of preventing the conflict from escalating. Major General Wood Kyle, commanding officer of the 3rd Marine Division was ordered to block Route 1 and stop Yeu's convoy. Kyle sent the 9th Marine Regiment. A platoon from 2nd Battalion supported by two M50 Ontos anti-tank vehicles purposely stalled a two and a half ton truck on the Thanh Quit Bridge nine miles from the Da Nang Air Base where the government troops were stationed. The truck blocked all traffic on the bridge and prevented the convoy from entering Da Nang.

Yeu was furious and determined. His forces vastly outgunned the American Marine platoon and were more than capable of removing the truck from the bridge. However, Yeu was not anxious to engage the Americans. As an alternative to a confrontation with the U.S. Marines, Yeu ordered the battalion's 155 mm howitzers to take up positions on the southern bank of the river and target the Marine headquarters at Da Nang Air Base which was within range.

General Walt was informed of the standoff and ordered Colonel John Chaisson to defuse the situation. Arriving at the scene by helicopter, Chaisson crossed the bridge and asked to speak with Yeu. He warned the ARVN commander that if his troops continued their advance or shelled the air base, the US forces would consider Yeu's actions as an attack on America and would respond accordingly. As he was talking, Chaisson had arranged for a flight of heavily armed Marine F-8E Crusaders to fly over the bridge. In addition, Chaisson informed Yeu that American artillery had already targeted Yeu's convoy and was prepared to fire if aggressive action was taken to cross the bridge. Chaisson, a veteran of two wars and a Harvard graduate, was calm but unmoving. He made it clear that Yeu's rebel forces would be destroyed if they proceeded toward Da Nang. He convinced Yeu that a civil war between ARVN forces would not be in anyone's interest and that the Viet Cong and NVA were ready to take advantage of the situation if allowed.

As a compromise, Yeu ordered his armor and artillery to return to Hoi An, but his troops remained in position across the river.

Ky knew that the Americans stepping in to protect the Da Nang Air Base would appear as weakness on his part. He needed to show strength to prevent any potential coups against his regime in Saigon. At the same time, he knew that dismissing any of the pro-Struggle Movement ARVN commanders could cause mass desertions and put Hue and Da Nang in peril of falling to the Viet Cong and NVA.

After considering the situation, Ky sent a private message to the commander involved in the bridge incident that if he and his troops returned to fighting the true enemy, he and the soldiers that followed them into rebellion would not be punished. Yeu accepted the offer and once again sent his forces to battle the Viet Cong and NVA around Hoi An. Ky then claimed that troops that had rebelled were an insignificant minority of the nation's ARVN forces and left it at that. For the moment the crisis seemed to be diverted. It didn't last.

White House – Washington D.C., USA

While the Pentagon kept them well informed, President Johnson's administration had kept a low profile during the stalemate on the bridge. The Struggle Movement was already anti-American and growing by the day. Johnson did not need to pour more kerosene on the fire. Many political cartoonists and commentators kept the story alive by blaming Johnson and his staff for enthusiastically supporting Ky making him appear to be an American puppet.

Dismayed that American allies in South Vietnam were fighting each other, Johnson was even more concerned that troops loyal to Thi might actually use the weapons that America had given them to attack U.S. troops. It was a public relations disaster in the making and had no shortage of critics ready to pounce once the first bullet was fired in anger.

Johnson complained to his staff and the Pentagon that Ky's remarks to the press that he would order the mayor of Da Nang shot for treason were "bad judgment" on Ky's behalf. Johnson seemed to be building a case for supporting Ky's removal and asked if anyone else knew other examples of poor behavior from the prime minister. General Maxwell Taylor said that while serving as the ambassador to South Vietnam in 1964, he had heard Ky comment that he had tremendous admiration for Adolf Hitler. Taylor added that he believed Ky had matured since his unfortunate comment.

While Johnson was pretending not to be involved with the dispute, Secretary of State Dean Rusk came out making a statement on the conflict and said, "This is in part an effort by some civilians to carve out a certain position in relation to the steps that have been announced for some time by the military government to move toward a constitutional system."

Preaching Buddhism, pacifism, nationalism, and neutralism, the Struggle Movement commanded wide support throughout South Vietnam but was especially strong in Central Vietnam. Ambassador Lodge wrote a cable to Johnson that the majority of the population supported the Struggle Movement including much of the regular army and many Catholic leaders. He went on to write that if free elections were held today then the candidates put forth by the Struggle Movement leaders would most likely win overwhelmingly. The Struggle Movement was an anti-communist movement but also demanded that South Vietnam should be neutral in the Cold War. This was unacceptable to the Americans who demanded South Vietnam's loyalty in its fight against Chinese and Soviet expansion of communism throughout the world. America wanted South Vietnam as a true ally if it was going to continue to provide military support and financial aid. Lodge went on to claim that a democratic, but neutral South Vietnam would be a disaster.

Struggle Movement rallies always included premade signs saying, "Stop killing our people" and "Foreign Countries Have No Right to Set Up Military Bases on Vietnamese Land." The protestors chanted, "Da Do My!" which meant "Down with the Americans!" Ky claimed that the Struggle Movement was nothing more than a Viet Cong front organization and that its Buddhist leaders were puppets of the Communists.

Both Lodge and Westmoreland supported Ky's claims. U.S. National Security Adviser Walt Rostow claimed that if the Struggle Movement came to power, the leaders would be unable to stop the Viet Cong from overthrowing the new government and taking control. Even though Ky was extremely unpopular with the South Vietnamese people, the United States was obligated to help Ky crush the Struggle Movement because it was the only way to prevent the communists from coming to power. Rostow's arguments were persuasive, and Johnson agreed.

Saigon, South Vietnam

Disappointed in General Chuan's performance during the bridge crisis, Ky asked the military junta to remove Chuan from command and replace him with General Ton That Dinh. Dinh was aggressive and was willing to suppress the Buddhists. The junta unanimously agreed. On April 15th Dinh flew to Hue.

Hue and Da Nang, South Vietnam

The Buddhist leaders were dismayed by Chuan's removal and Dinh's appointment. They declared the country to be in a state of emergency and demanded civilian rule immediately. Knowing that their demands would most likely be refused the leaders called for protests throughout the country to escalate.

Dinh retook control of the radio stations in Hue and Da Nang by negotiating with the protestors. He agreed to allow them a specified amount of airtime each day in exchange for leaving the stations peacefully. He also convinced the Mayor of Da Nang to accept Saigon's authority. Things seemed to be calming down when a clash erupted between the

Buddhists and the Viet Nam Quoc Dan Dang, the Vietnam Nationalist Party that supported the continuation of the war against the communists. Dinh was forced to intervene and used his troops to restrain the two groups. Tensions in the two cities eased once again.

Having been embarrassed by his failed assault on the leaders of the Struggle Movement, Ky was looking for a way to gain face through a show of force. Without informing President Thieu or General Westmoreland, Ky ordered General Cao Van Vien to fly South Vietnamese marines and airborne units to Da Nang and take control of the local ARVN headquarters placing the commanders under arrest. They succeeded.

When reports of the early morning assault on Da Nang arrived in Washington, the Pentagon called General Walt for an update on the situation. Hearing the news from his superiors, Walt was angry at Ky for not giving him a warning about what he was planning.

Ky ignored the American commander and ordered planes to fly over the rebel forces in the city and drop messages that threatened to destroy any rebel soldiers or civilians that shot at the Saigon troops in the assault force.

Hearing the news of the assault, the Viet Cong leaders wisely decided to stay out of the fight between their enemy forces and hoped for as much death and destruction as possible. The Viet Cong didn't want to weaken either side's desire and focus on killing the other side. And the best part was that the death toll that would surely ensue cost them nothing.

Dinh was surprised and confused by Ky's move. He believed he was carrying out Ky and the junta's orders by restoring peace. He decided to be safe and abandoned his post at the air base. He fled to General Walt's headquarters. He asked the American general for help and was immediately flown to Hue where the pro-Buddhist forces were still in control of the city and air base.

Later that day, two VNAF aircraft strafed the rebel forces located near the U.S. Marine positions to the north of Da Nang. General Ky's surprise assault would have quickly led to open fighting between the ARVN rebels and the ARVN government loyalists. The Americans were caught in the middle of what had become a civil war within a civil war.

Wanting to avoid as much bloodshed as possible, General Walt asked the military junta in Saigon to withdraw Ky's loyalist forces from Da Nang.

When he got word of the American general's request, Ky was furious at Walt for going around him and denied his request to remove his troops. He told Walt that the Americans should stay out of South Vietnam's politics and internal skirmishes. Ky replaced General Dinh with General Huynh Van Cao, a Catholic and former President Diem loyalist.

The next day, Cao was accompanied by U.S. Colonel Hamblen, the senior advisor in I Corps, and Brigadier General Platt, Chief of Staff to III MAF, on his way to Hue to visit the headquarters of ARVN 1st Division. Karen asked if she could accompany them. Plat thought it was a good idea to let the public know what was going on and gave her permission. She climbed on board their helicopter.

Hearing of the new I Corps commander's presence,

local Buddhist protestors and pro-Thi ARVN troops rioted and broke into the 1st Division headquarters. Karen shot an entire roll of film in less than two minutes. The anger of the rioters was clear on their faces.

Cao, Karen, and the American officers quickly boarded a helicopter that was to take them back to Da Nang Air Base. Karen reloaded her camera and continued snapping shots out of the helicopter's open doorway at the angry mob below.

As the helicopter was lifting off, a rebel ARVN lieutenant removed his service pistol from its holster and fired at the helicopter. Karen took his photo as the end of his pistol barrel flared. Two bullets hit the helicopter right next to Karen's head. She wasn't sure if the rebel officer was shooting at her or the helicopter. She fell backward onto the deck to get out of the way, but she kept her wits and continued to take photos from inside the helicopter. The U.S. Army door gunner opened fire with his M60 machine gun. The rebel lieutenant was riddled with bullets and fell dead. Two more rebel soldiers standing next to the officer were also hit by the door gunner's bullets and seriously wounded. No one in the helicopter was hurt. Karen moved to the open doorway once again and snapped photos of the dead and wounded rebels on the ground. It was an incredible moment when South Vietnamese soldiers and American soldiers exchanged gunfire for the first time. She captured it... a big moment in history. The door gunner turned back to her and said, "Did you get it?"

"Yeah. I think so," said Karen.

"Can I get a copy?"

"Sure, write your name and unit on a piece of paper

and I'll see that you get a copy once the photos are developed."

The door gunner grinned as if he had just won the lottery. "If it's not too much to ask, I'd like a copy too," said Plat.

"Yeah, me too," said Hamblen.

"Us too," said the pilot and co-pilot.

Karen laughed and said, "Of course."

She could feel the adrenaline still coursing through her body. She felt so alive and although she didn't want to admit it… addicted to danger.

Rallying against the Americans, the Struggle Movement leaders accused American forces of unfitting interference in an internal South Vietnamese quarrel.

Still angry about General Walt's interference, Ky refused to remove his forces and seek a peaceful solution to the conflict. He relished the opportunity to confront the American military which he considered was overstepping their authority. He ordered his artillery commanders to aim all of their 155mm howitzers at the U.S. Marine base. His orders were to destroy the Marine base if the Americans took any action to hinder the loyalist aircraft from completing their missions.

After two days of fighting, Ky forces retook much of the city center, including the government building and the radio station, then slowly pushed the rebel forces to the Tourane River just outside of the city. Ky's air superiority played a big part in driving the rebel troops while destroying their armored vehicles and artillery.

The rebel soldiers seized the bridge and a nearby ammunition depot containing 6,000 tons of ammunition. They placed mines on the steel supports under the bridge and wired the ammunition depot with explosives.

Shortly after the rebel engineers finished, government troops approached the bridge from the west ready to fight their way across. The rebel gunners on the opposite side of the river warned the government troops that the bridge was minded, then opened fire with their recoilless rifles and machine guns.

Fearful that the bridge which was mostly used by American forces would be destroyed in the fighting, General Walt once again sent Colonel Chaisson to reason with both sides and avoid more conflict.

Chaisson was successful in convincing Ky's forces to pull back and relieved them with a company of U.S. Marines on the western side of the bridge. Chaisson then approached the rebel commander on the eastern side of the bridge and asked for permission to place his marines on his side of the structure. The commander refused and said he would blow up the bridge if the American Marines attempted to cross. Chaisson ignored the rebel commander and placed his Marines on the eastern side of the river. His men simply sat among the rebel soldiers without using any force.

A few minutes later, General Walt arrived on the western side of the river and walked with Colonel Chaisson to the opposite side of the bridge. Before they could reach the opposite side, a rebel officer ordered them to stop and threatened to blow up the bridge if they failed to do so. To add credibility to the threat, rebel machine gunners fired their weapons over the heads of the American Marines which were forced to duck. At that point, things got a bit tense. Walt began debating with the officer who threatened to blow up the bridge as if calling his bluff. The officer reacted by saying, "General, we will all die together." The officer signaled a military engineer who plunged the detonator... and nothing happened.

What the officer and engineer did not know was that Chaisson had sent a unit of engineers under the bridge when the Marines began crossing to the other side. The engineers had cut all the wire leading to the mines before Chaisson and Walt ever set foot on the bridge. Another unit of engineers had defused the explosive in the ammunition depot. With unhappy American Marines mixed in with the rebel forces and his options limited, the rebel commander decided it would be the better part of valor if his men retreated. The standoff was over, but the civil war was still intense.

The ARVN rebels supporting the Struggle Movement still held defensive positions in Da Nang and were still fighting the loyalist government ARVN. The longer the fighting continued, the weaker Ky seemed. He had enough and ordered airstrikes against the rebel forces within Da Nang.

Karen stood on the tarmac and watched the government aircraft being armed. She asked a nearby Marine what was going on. He replied, "Ky is gonna kick some rebel ass."

She raised her camera snapped a photo, then moved closer knowing that no civilians were supposed to be on base and that the South Vietnamese soldiers guarding the aircraft could fire on her. She took the risk. A guard moved forward with his rifle in his hands and stood in front of her. She froze in her tracks. He said something in Vietnamese that she didn't understand. He waved his arm at the aircraft behind him, then grinned. He wanted his photo taken with the aircraft in the background. She nodded and took two photos. The soldier seemed satisfied. She smiled and moved past him to get a better shot of the ground crews loading the rockets and bombs on the aircraft.

Karen was an experienced photojournalist with a good eye for composition. But that wasn't her real talent. She had a knack for being at the right place at the right time. It was her life she was risking, and she felt she had a right to follow her instincts. She followed her intuition even when it didn't make sense. She could live with not getting a story. Sometimes that was inevitable. But she couldn't live with not being true to herself.

When General Walt received news that Ky's aircraft were armed with rockets and bombs, he grew concerned about civilian casualties. There were still over 1,000 Americans in Da Nang. Walt phoned General Cao with his concerns, but Cao was afraid the men under his command would kill him if he tried to call off the airstrikes. He fled to Walt's headquarters and asked for asylum in the United States for himself and his family.

Walt went to see the VNAF commander at Da Nang Air Base hoping to talk some sense into him and get him to call off the air assault. It was no use. Loaded with rockets and bombs, the loyalist jets took off and headed for Da Nang.

Returning to his headquarters in the Marine compound, Walt ordered the commander of 1st Marine Aircraft Wing to prepare four American jets for air-to-air combat.

Before the American jets were ready, the rebels in the city near U.S. Marine units fired their machine guns at the loyalist aircraft. Two of the VNAF aircraft responded by firing rockets at the rebel positions. They missed the rebels and three rockets hit the American positions, wounding eight U.S. Marines.

Furious but constrained, Walt ordered two American fighter jets armed with air-to-air missiles into the air. Their mission was to tail the loyalist aircraft and shoot them down if they fired on Da Nang.

As the American aircraft took off, the VNAF commander responded to the new American threat by sending more of his aircraft into the sky to tail the American aircraft.

Walt would not be deterred and sent two more American aircraft to tail the VNAF aircraft tailing the American aircraft. While the VNAF aircraft had machine guns and air-to-ground rockets, the American aircraft had air-to-air missiles and could easily defeat the more numerous VNAF aircraft. After two hours of playing chicken in the skies over Da Nang and nobody firing at their ally, the VNAF aircraft finally broke off and returned to base.

A short time later, Washington received a complaint from the military junta in Saigon saying that General Walt had unlawfully interfered with South Vietnamese politics. When questioned, Walt explained in detail what had happened and the basis for his command decisions. The Pentagon gave Walt permission to act as he saw fit and informed the junta that Walt was correct in his actions.

Acting as a liaison, Westmoreland met with Ky and Thi in hopes of ending their squabble and getting back to fighting the Viet Cong and NVA. During the meeting, Thi agreed to support Ky and end his opposition to the government. At Ky's request, Thi agreed to leave the country permanently, so he was no longer a threat to Ky's rule. In exchange, Thi requested that Cao be allowed to return to the command of I Corps. Ky agreed.

Before leaving South Vietnam, Thi tried to convince Cao to return to his command of I Corps. Concerned for his family, Cao refused. He was determined to go to the United States and join the American military. Disheartened, Thi suggested General Hoang Xuan Lam as his replacement. Ky and the junta agreed.

Thi left South Vietnam. General Lam focused on fighting the Viet Cong and NVA instead of the rebels and the Americans. It took great patience from Westmoreland not to reprimand Ky for having fired on American troops during the conflict. Fortunately for Ky, Westmoreland was more interested in fighting the communists than punishing a South Vietnamese prime minister.

Even though the rebel ARVN were no longer involved in the revolt, Ky's marines continued to have street battles with protestors in Da Nang until the Struggle Movement finally collapsed. Before ending their insurrection, the protestors burned the American Consulate in Hue.

By June 19th, the old imperial capital was once again under the control of the South Vietnamese government and streets grew quiet. Everyone was exhausted and no longer had the will to fight... until the next time. It was a clear victory for Ky and the military junta except for the damage to their relationship with the Americans.

Over 150 Vietnamese were killed and another 700 were wounded during the uprising. The Americans had twenty-three wounded, but no deaths. The collapse of the Buddhist rebellion ended the Buddhists as a political force. The South Vietnamese government grew in strength and resolve now that the Buddhists were out of the picture.

ARC LIGHT

April 12, 1966 – Mu Gia Pass, North Vietnam

High above the clouds, twenty-nine B-52s nicknamed "Buffs" flew in formation from Guam's Anderson Air Base. Flying at 30,000 feet, the flight was a mix of B-52Fs and the newly modified "Big Bellied" B52Ds with their expanded bomb bays and capable of carrying twice the bomb load. They were headed for the Mu Gia Pass in the Annamite Mountain Range between Laos and North Vietnam. The pass connected Route 15 from Quang Binh Province in North Vietnam with Route 12 in Khammouane Province in Laos.

The pass was the main point of entry into the Ho Chi Minh Trail running through Laos. The road threaded itself along a narrow steep-sided valley surrounded by dog-toothed limestone peaks and flat-topped plateaus. A dense jungle canopy covered the entire area making aerial observation difficult if not impossible. Because of its difficult terrain, the pass was seen as a choke point by MACV and the CIA. It was estimated that seventy-five percent of truck traffic into Laos traveled through the pass. If the U.S. Air Force could find a way to cut off the pass, supplies, weapons, and ammunition flowing into South Vietnam would be drastically reduced.

To thwart the Viet Cong and NVA in the South, the American Air Force planners put together the largest bombing mission since World War II. The Buffs would use a combination of 500, 750, & 1000 lb. subsurface and delayed fuse bombs designed to create landslides from the steep slopes that would wipe out the road and permanently block it with an enormous amount of boulders and dirt. The planners believed the thick vegetation from the slopes would create a kind of web holding the newly fallen rocks and soil in place and making the mess impossible to move.

As the heavy bombers reached their target, they unleashed over 500 tons of bombs on the pass. When detonated, the bombs did exactly as the planners had expected and created multiple avalanches all across the pass destroying the road and creating the world's biggest mess. What the planners had not accounted for was Ho Chi Minh's Ant Army.

Within hours, thousands of civilian volunteers arrived in the valley by truck, bicycle, and on foot. They went to work like a collective hive-mind, each person understanding their role in the grand scheme. The pass was not only cleared in ten hours, but the first convoy of trucks filled with supplies, weapons, and reinforcements was also on its way once again. It was an incredible feat of raw manpower.

As a precautionary measure, the North Vietnamese built a series of alternative routes to bypass the Mu Gia Pass. They even built a series of petrol and lubricant pipelines to refuel the trucks once they were through the pass. Almost all of it was done by hand and shovel using reinforced bicycles with saddlebags to carry away the debris from the bombings and construction.

The CIA reported that the communists would spare no effort to keep the pass open and the Ho Chi Minh Trail full of supply and transport caravans. Despite the frequent bombing of the pass, the U.S. Air Force and Navy were unable to keep the pass closed for any sustained period of time. It was like a giant snake that couldn't be killed.

As time went on, the North Vietnamese installed more than 300 large caliber anti-aircraft gun emplacements to defend the pass. Later, they even installed SAM-2 missile sites to cover the various aircraft approaches to the pass forcing the bombers and gunships to keep their distance or risk being blown out of the sky.

Realizing that conventional bombs could not do the job, the Pentagon considered using tactical nuclear weapons to block the pass for good. They decided against it when they realized that using such weapons would give the Soviets and Chinese license to use tactical nuclear weapons themselves, or worse, provide them to the Viet Cong for use against the ARVN and the Americans in the South.

April 18, 1966 – Dong Hai, North Vietnam

Wild Weasel (WW) is the code name given to any USAF aircraft equipped with anti-radiation missiles designed to destroy enemy SAM installations. Developed by the United States Air Force after the introduction of Soviet SAMS into the Vietnam theatre and responsible for downing multiple U.S. aircraft operating as part of Operation Rolling Thunder.

The Wild Weasel's main tactic was to bait the enemy

anti-aircraft defenses into targeting the Wild Weasel aircraft with its radar. The Wild Weasel's electronics would trace back the enemy radar waves to their source and then send that signal to its weapon – the AGM-45 Shrike air-to-ground missile. The Shrike would then target the enemy's anti-aircraft defenses.

The main problem with the AGM-45 Shrike missile used by the Wild Weasels was its limited range of seven miles. The SA-2 missiles used in the enemy radar and launching system it hunted had an effective range of twenty-eight miles meaning that if a threat was detected the enemy could fire on and kill the American aircraft before it ever fired. Fortunately, the aircraft's countermeasures could pick up early warning emissions 100 miles out from the enemy SAM site. This gave the pilots time to take evasive action including flying on the deck dangerously close to the jungle canopy to prevent from being spotted.

In addition, the Shrike missile had no memory of where the SA-2 launcher was located, so if the enemy shut off the radar, the Shrike lost its homing signal and would wander aimlessly missing the target. It was far from an ideal weapon system, but it was a great improvement over the unguided rocket being used to destroy SAM sites.

The Americans tried different aircraft platforms for the Wild Weasel program and finally settled on the F-105 Thunderchief. When modified with the electronic countermeasures needed to guide the Shrike missiles, the Thunderchief was given the designation F-105G or Wild Weasel III. A total of sixty-one Thunderchiefs were eventually upgraded to F-105G specifications. The Thunderchiefs would operate in hunter-killer teams where one aircraft would identify the enemy radar at the SAM site and the other aircraft would attack the site from a different angle. The teams were primarily used to clear the way for Rolling Thunder bombing missions. The F-105Gs operated out of two air bases in Thailand near the Laotian border – Udorn and Ubon.

Flying in front of a bomber squadron, the weapon's officer in a Wild Weasel picked up an early warning radar signal from a source ahead. Without getting closer, the weapons officer could not accurately locate the SA-2's Fan Song radar. The pilot continued with caution knowing that the SA-2 system could fire a missile at any time.

As the target came within range but well before he could see it, the weapons officer fired a Shrike anti-radiation missile. On its way down the missile disappeared into a haze over the target area. Moments later, the weapons officer saw the radar suddenly stop emitting a signal. They had hit it and at the very least had damaged it, so it was no longer operational. It was the first successful launch of an AGM-45 Shrike missile.

Even with the first official victory of the weapon, the Wild Weasel program was fraught with problems. The aircraft were being shot down by enemy fighters and gunfire at an alarming rate. By August of 1966, only four of the eleven F-105s in Thailand were still operational. The others had been lost or damaged beyond repair. The Americans still had a lot to learn about destroying the SAM sites and the lessons were costly.

May 1, 1966 – Tay Ninh Province, South Vietnam

A Company from 2nd Infantry Regiment, 10th Mountain Division patrolled along the eastern edge of the Cai Bac River. The terminus of the Ho Chi Minh Trail, Tay Ninh Province was a major entry point into the South. The American patrols often included treks through the rubber and sugar plantations that dotted the area. The Cai Bac River was also the border between South Vietnam and Cambodia. It was well-known that the Viet Cong had camps on the other side of the river in Cambodian territory. There was little the Americans could do about the camps except to patrol along the river in hopes of catching an enemy unit crossing over into South Vietnam.

As the American soldiers approached a bend in the river, mortar shells exploded around them wounding several soldiers. The U.S. Company spread out searching for the Viet Cong mortar position but found nothing. A scout sighted puffs of smoke from mortar tubes on the Cambodian side of the river. The Cambodian Army knew that the Viet Cong had camps along the border but did nothing to kick them out as long as they didn't travel too far inland. The Cambodian military was not looking for a war.

Hearing the scout's report, the American commander realized the implications of what he was about to do. Under the rules of engagement, the Americans had a right to defend themselves. The commander had little choice. The American soldiers would not run from the Viet Cong even if they were in Cambodia.

The commander ordered his mortar units to fire across the river at the Viet Cong positions. For several minutes, mortar shells from both sides flew across the river. It was the Viet Cong that finally fell silent. The Americans had no way of knowing if they had destroyed the VC mortars or if the VC had retreated. It didn't matter. It was a skirmish that could have started another war but didn't. The first U.S. attack on Cambodia was over. Everyone wanted to forget about it as soon as possible. The Americans and the Cambodians had no interest in expanding the war. The Cambodian Army continued to keep its head buried in the sand and ignored the Viet Cong.

PAUL REVERE

May 10, 1966 – Pleiku, South Vietnam

Sightings of a large NVA force west of Duc Co and Plei Me Special Forces Camps caught MACV's attention. Nobody was sure if it was an opportunity or a trap, but most assumed it would be both. The Americans were anxious to engage large enemy forces, especially in areas where airpower and artillery could be brought to bear.

The North Vietnamese were also eager to engage the Americans. The airbase at Pleiku supported much of Central Vietnam and was considered a prime target. To attack Pleiku, the NVA needed to destroy the Special Forces camps near the Cambodian border that protected the airbase and acted as an early warning system for potential assaults. The Special Forces were constantly patrolling around their camps and were difficult to get past. They were also a powerful enemy force to leave behind and risk attack from the rear or flanks of any assault force.

MACV dispatched the U.S. 3rd Brigade, 25th Infantry Division to sweep the area and find the enemy force. The 3rd Brigade was deployed to Landing Zone Oasis west of Duc Co. After a week of searching and finding nothing, the brigade commander changed direction and focused on the area west of the Chu Pong Massif. With the change of direction, the NVA could no longer avoid the Americans. It was time to fight.

A CIDG company made up of Montagnard warriors and U.S. Special Forces advisers finally made contact with two battalions of NVA seven miles southwest of Plei Djereng Camp. As it engaged the enemy, the CIDG company was quickly reinforced by two more CIDG companies. The fighting continued throughout the day with neither side making much progress. When darkness fell, the fighting tapered off and both sides dug in for the night.

Early the next morning, the NVA attacked the CIDG positions. Knowing that they were outnumbered and at risk of being flanked by unseen reinforcements the CIDG commanders decided they would stand a much better chance of survival behind the earthen walls of the Special Forces Camp at Plei Djereng. The CIDG withdrew from their defense positions and carried out a running firefight with the NVA. The CIDG lost eighteen Montagnard and two Special Forces advisers.

When the CIDG reached the camp, the NVA were unwilling to assault the fortified defenses of the Special Forces and brought their chase to an end. But they weren't finished with their enemy and proceeded to mortar the camp relentlessly. The NVA killed an additional thirty Montagnard and wounded fifty-four.

A World War II veteran commander, Brigadier General Glenn Walker sent 2nd Battalion, 35th

Infantry Regiment to reinforce Plei Djereng Camp. The battalion flew to Landing Zones Eleven Alfa and Ten Alfa. When sixty-three men from Company B landed on Ten Alfa, they immediately came under heavy fire and the landing zone was closed to further helicopter landings. The NVA attacked again and again hoping to destroy the company before reinforcements arrived. The soldiers in Company B fought off the enemy assaults. Supporting fire finally drove back the NVA enough that the rest of Company B and Company A, 1st Battalion, 35th Infantry Regiment were able to land on Ten Alfa and reinforce the Americans already there. As the fighting died down with the setting sun, the American forces dug in for the night.

Just after midnight, the NVA 66th Regiment assaulted LZ Ten Alfa while NVA 33rd Regiment attacked Landing Zone Eleven Alfa. It was a fierce fight, but the Americans were able to repulse both assaults. At dawn, the soldiers on LZ Ten Alfa found over eighty enemy bodies spread around their defensive perimeter.

When the Americans attempted to move beyond the perimeter of LZ Ten Alfa, they ran into the NVA main front line and were driven back to the landing zone. Minutes later, the NVA launched a brutal mortar attack on the landing zone. When the mortar attack ended, the NVA again assaulted the landing zone multiple times and were again beaten back by the Americans. The NVA lost over 250 soldiers in the assaults.

Over the next eight days, the 3rd Brigade searched for the enemy but found no one. Walker assumed they had moved back across the border into Cambodia.

Walker again switched focus back to the Chu Pong Massif. Seven miles north of the Chu Pong Massif, a reconnaissance platoon from 2/35th Infantry spotted a group of NVA soldiers moving through the jungle. Hoping to find the main body, they followed the enemy group and fell into an ambush. The Americans were pinned down by heavy gunfire and radioed for reinforcements. The rest of the battalion and Troop C 3rd Squadron, 4th Cavalry Regiment came to their rescue and drove the NVA from the battlefield. The Americans had three killed and fourteen wounded from the skirmish.

A few days later, another reconnaissance platoon from 1/35th Infantry was patrolling near the Cambodian border when it came under heavy fire. The Americans called in air and artillery support forcing the enemy to withdraw. The Americans followed the NVA troops as they retreated toward Cambodia, a safe haven. The Americans ran into a well-entrenched enemy position and were again pinned down and unable to advance.

The American platoon was reinforced by two companies and a Brigade armored cavalry troop. The two sides pounded away at each other for the rest of the day. When the sun set, the NVA slipped from their entrenched positions and escaped across the border into Cambodia.

Fighting near the border was frustrating for the Americans because the enemy could easily retreat into Cambodia if the battle was not going their way. This drastically shortened the battle and cut down on NVA losses.

The results of Operation Paul Revere were an anemic victory for the Americans which had successfully driven the enemy from the battlefield. The American losses were sixty-six killed while the North Vietnamese had 546 killed and another sixty-eight captured. The problem was not the kill ratio. It was the number of troops and resources the Americans needed to commit to battle to defeat the NVA.

TEN YEARS OF CHAOS

May 16, 1966 – People's Republic of China

China was North Vietnam's biggest ally and supplied much of the aid that kept North Vietnamese and Viet Cong troops in the field. It was little wonder that North Vietnamese leaders grew concerned when they observed a major change in China's stability as Mao Zedong launched the "Cultural Revolution." It seemed that China was once again turning inward to purge capitalist and traditionalist remnants from Chinese society.

While Mao was still the Chairman of the Chinese Communist Party, the center of power in China, he had taken a step back after the failure of the Great Leap Forward campaign and the Great Chinese Famine that followed that debacle. He had recognized it was time for less radical leadership to take the reins and guide China forward. He seceded his control over the government and stayed quiet for five years until he realized that China was heading back to its capitalistic and traditional roots. It was too much for a man that had sacrificed everything to usher in communism, the basis of a just society.

The beginning of the Cultural Revolution marked a commanding return of Mao to power and the Cultural Revolution Group that would eventually replace the Secretariate and the Five Man Group that were effectively controlling the government. Mau charged that bourgeois factions had infiltrated the government and society. Their aim was to restore capitalism.

Those that attempted to stand in Mao's way didn't live long. Mao had effectively deputized the young people in China to rebel against the government and bombard the communist headquarters. The youth responded by forming "Red Guard" groups around the country that obeyed Mao's edicts like they were words from God. They published a compilation of Mao's greatest sayings in the "Little Red Book" which quickly became a sacred text for Mao's personality cult. The Red Guard held denunciation rallies against the revisionists and accused them publicly of betraying their country in the quest for gold. The youth organization seized power from local governments and installed their own leaders, many of which were in their teens and early twenties.

While Mao and his Red Guard were successful at purging many of the revisionist elements in the government, it came at a heavy cost. China's Cultural Revolution was plagued by violence and chaos. Millions died. The intellectual elites were the first to have their heads placed on the chopping blocks. Schools and universities were shut down and college entrance exams were canceled. Over ten million urban intellectual youths were sent to the countryside to work on farms and build infrastructure projects with their hands. It was back-breaking work and many teenagers unaccustomed to hard labor committed suicide. A brain-drain set China back decades. The revolutionary committees formed from the Red Guard and other youth groups often split into rival factions and resorted to armed fights between one another that became known as "violent struggles." During the Red August of Beijing, huge massacres took place throughout the nation, including the Guangxi Massacre, the Inner Mongolia Incident, the Guangdong Massacre, the Yunnan Massacre, and the Hunan Massacres. Without regard for China's historical heritage, the Red Guard youth destroyed relics and artifacts that they found offensive and ransacked cultural and religious sites. Tens of millions of Chinese were persecuted, imprisoned, and tortured. Many were assigned hard labor and died from exhaustion and starvation.

While the Americans were uneasy at the instability caused by Mao's cultural revolution, they also saw it as an opportunity to drive a wedge between the North Vietnamese and the Chinese. The only question was how? Mao did not seem concerned with anything the Americans were doing at the moment. Diplomatic cables went unanswered. China's borders were tighter than ever, and few foreigners were allowed into the country. It was like Mao had put a curtain around the country while he did what needed to be done. He didn't care what the foreign press reported or what the U.N. had to say. The revolution was an internal matter, and the Chinese capitalists would be dealt with one way or another. There was too much at stake to turn back. The Americans finally took the position of sitting back and watching as things unfolded with China and proclamations were announced by Mao and his Red Guard. President Johnson avoided any action that might cause the Chinese to lose focus as they were destroying each other. Johnson knew a gift horse when he saw one. There was no need to check the animal's teeth. Even with the internal violence, China was still a major opponent of the US. Nobody could tell how Mao would react to any external pressure. The great leader had his own agenda that kept changing as events inside China evolved. It was best to stay out of his way and enjoy the chaos while it lasted. The one thing the White House didn't want was for China to enter the war in Vietnam.

Hanoi watched with trepidation as the blood flowed and the weapon and ammunition factories ground to a halt throughout China. The North Vietnamese politburo wondered if there would be anything left of the great nation when Mao and his followers were finally through. To increase their influence over Southeast Asia, the Soviets were only too happy to take up some of the slack as the Chinese faltered. It wasn't enough. The revolution in Vietnam suffered but the determined North Vietnamese and Viet Cong fought on to unite their country under a communist flag. They had survived hard times before and they would survive this time. Seeing how their countrymen suffered, the Revolution could not wait.

June 2, 1966 – Tu Mo Rong, South Vietnam

The monsoon rains had come to the Central Highlands. Taking advantage of the thick layer of cloud cover over Kon Tum Province, the NVA and Viet Cong launched a major offensive. The communists laid siege to Tu Mo Rong thirty-two miles northeast of Dak

To where the ARVN 42nd Regiment, 22nd Division was located.

The land was covered with brown-water rice paddies and dense jungle that made patrolling in the area exhausting as the soldiers' feet sank deep in the rain-saturated mud. Seized by suction, many American boots, and Vietnamese sandals were lost never to be seen again. The constant rain didn't make things easier. With little chance of drying out, mold covered and rotted everything including feet.

General Westmoreland had already promised to contest any enemy incursions into the area. In response to the invasion, the Americans launched Operation Hawthorne utilizing three battalions from the 1st Brigade, 101st Airborne Division, a battalion from the 1st Cavalry Division, and two CIDG companies. The field commander was Brigadier General Willard Pearson, a World War II veteran. Pearson was a big advocate of night operations and long-range reconnaissance patrols to determine the enemy's position and strength. One of Pearson's subordinates, Major David Hackworth took the semi-guerrila tactics to heart and developed "Tiger Force," a platoon-sized recon unit of forty-five paratroopers that operated deep in enemy territory and was tasked to "out guerrilla the guerrillas." The soldiers in Tiger Force were not only experienced at long-range reconnaissance but hard-hitting. The highly decorated unit quickly developed a reputation of "getting at the enemy" but often paid for their aggressive tactics with heavy casualties.

Karen and Jerry Sanger, an AP war correspondent, had been embedded with Company C, 2nd Battalion,

502nd Infantry Regiment for the duration of the operation. The 2nd Battalion was part of the task force moving to break the siege around Tu Mo Rong and relieve the South Vietnamese 42nd Regiment. There was definitely going to be fighting and that made Karen both excited and apprehensive. It was why she had come to Vietnam but that didn't help her nerves. She still had a lot to learn about moving through enemy territory and how to spot booby traps.

Battle was always unpredictable and dangerous, especially for a photojournalist that liked to get close. Karen took to heart the great war photographer Robert Capa's advice, "If your pictures aren't good enough, you aren't close enough."

In spite of her fears, Karen forced herself to take risks that she knew might kill or seriously wound her. She would prefer the former. In her mind, death was preferable to being grossly disfigured or permanently crippled. The possibility was always there, but she wouldn't let it stop her from taking the photo from "inside the action," a style that had become her trademark.

Sanger was a bit of a smartass, but Karen still liked him. He just took some getting used to. Besides, he was a good journalist and cared deeply about the war. Karen admired that. He was also attractive in a nerdy kind of way and his muscles were toned from years of walking in country. He wore glasses with thick frames that he kept tied around the back of his head so he wouldn't lose them in the middle of a firefight. Sanger was blind without his glasses. The world became a big ball of fuzz.

Karen was in good shape physically, but nothing could have prepared her for the monsoons of

Southeast Asia and the mud that accompanied them. She was lucky. She didn't weigh much, and her rucksack was not loaded down with heavy ammunition. The multiple bandoleers of M-60 bullets that most of the soldiers carried on patrol would have brought Karen to her knees. But even with her lighter load, her feet sank deep in the mud just like everyone else's. She hated walking through the brown water rice paddies where she could not see where she was stepping. She was sure something bad was down there waiting to break her ankle or pierce her boot. It was while she was crossing a rice paddy that Karen got stuck.

She had just pulled her boot out of a foot of mud when she stepped forward and her leg sank up to her crotch in mud. Losing her balance by the sudden shift, she thought she was going to topple over, but her leg was encased in the mud allowing her to regain her balance and remain upright. She cursed the rice paddy and its mud. Sanger came up beside her and said, "Are you okay?"

"Yeah, I'm fine. Just stuck in the fucking mud," said Karen.

"Which foot?"

"Left."

"All right. I'll help pull you out."

"Thanks. This is kinda embarrassing."

"This is Vietnam. Getting stuck in the mud is just par for the course."

Sanger pushed his hands down in the water and mud, then grabbed her thigh. Holding her camera bag above the water, Karen attempted to lift her leg, but she had no leverage. Sanger pulled. She didn't move. "Wow. You really are stuck," said Sanger giving up.

"You need to break the suction," said a soldier passing by but not helping.

"How am I supposed to do that?" said Karen.

"A stick or tree branch," said the soldier as he moved on.

"Not a bad idea," said Sanger. "Let me see what I can find."

"What am I supposed to do in the meantime?"

"Try not to attract the enemy. You're kinda a sitting duck."

Jerry trudged over to the closest dike, hiked up the embankment, and moved off in search of something to break the suction. Karen watched as the last of the patrol exited the rice paddy and disappeared over the embankment. "Hey, you guys ain't gonna leave us, are you?" said Karen.

She heard no response. There was no one in sight and she felt very lonely. Sanger was right. She was a sitting duck. The only sound was the pattering of raindrops hitting the muddy water. After five more minutes, Sanger reappeared with a wooden pole he had snagged from a farmer's fence and said, "Let's see if this does the job."

"You sound like there is a possibility that it won't, and I'll be stuck here until I rot."

"Always a possibility."

"You're not helping, Jerry."

"I never said I was a cheerleader."

"Obviously you are not."

"Okay. Here's the plan. I'm gonna shove this thing down the side of your leg until it goes past your boot. That should break the suction and you can pull your leg out."

"Okay. Are you sure it's gonna work?"

"Only one way to find out."

Sanger pushed the pole down in the mud using Karen's leg as a guide. "Hey, be careful with that thing. I'm a delicate flower."

"You want out?"

"Yeah, but I don't want to lose my leg in the process."

"Don't be a drama queen. At most, you'll lose a couple of toes. Almost there…"

"Okay, you're at my boot. Give it another six inches."

Sanger pushed down more, and the pole sank another six inches. "That should do it," said Sanger. "See if you can pull your leg out."

Karen attempted to pull her leg out with Sanger's help, but it still didn't budge. Sanger moved the pole around attempting to break the suction. Nothing. "Dammit! Now what?" said Karen.

"I think I should shoot ya and put you out of your misery," said Sanger.

"You're an asshole, Jerry."

"Shut up and let me think. Can you wiggle your foot out of your boot?"

"No. It's laced up."

"Maybe I could cut the laces."

"How?"

"My pocketknife at the end of the pole."

"That's a bad idea, Jerry. You'll cut me."

"A little… probably. But it's better than staying out here in the middle of nothing."

"Yeah. You're right. Just be careful… and stop when I scream."

"I need something to attach it."

Karen reached into her camera bag and pulled out

a spool of electrical tape that she used to seal her film canisters. "How about this?" said Karen.

"Perfect," said Sanger attaching his pocketknife, blade open, to the end of the pole with the rubbery tape.

"Let me do it," said Karen handing him her camera bag and taking the pole.

She slowly lowered the end of the pole into the brown water and used her leg to guide it down to her boot. "You really don't want to cut yourself. The farmers use human shit as fertilizer for the rice," said Sanger.

"I know you think you're being helpful, Jerry, but you're not. Silence is golden."

"Right."

Karen reached her boot with the knife. She couldn't see what she was doing but imagined where the shoelaces would be and shoved the knife blade downward. "I think I've got one," said Karen moving the pole up and down. The shoelace snapped in two.

"My foot moved," said Karen surprised.

"That's good. Is it enough?" said Sanger as he set the camera bag on the edge of the dike embankment.

"Not yet. I'll cut a couple more laces."

Karen continued to cut until she could wiggle her foot. She pulled up the pole and handed it to Sanger. He held the pole horizontally and said, "Grab this and I'll pull."

Karen grabbed onto the pole with both hands and Sanger pulled. After a few moments, her foot slipped out of the boot. It took another minute to pull her leg out of the mud. She was free. "Nice job!" said Sanger.

"How am I supposed to get my boot back?" said Karen.

"You're not. It's a goner."

"Bullshit. I paid $26 for those things. 'Sides, how am I supposed to walk?"

"Hop?"

"Goddammit, Jerry."

"I'm sure the battalion quartermaster has an extra pair of boots."

"And where in the hell is the quartermaster?"

"Back at the base, but the radioman can have a pair brought in with the next helicopter supply run."

"That's great, Jerry. That's just great. What am I supposed to do in the meantime?"

"And here I thought you were gonna say 'Thanks.'"

"You're right. Thanks. And I take back the 'Asshole' comment."

"Why? I kinda like being an asshole."

They moved to the embankment and Karen picked up her camera bag. She hobbled up the side of the dike with Sanger's help and disappeared over the other side. Karen felt lucky she still had her sock, but it wasn't much protection when she stepped on a rock. It also didn't offer much traction as it too was covered in mud.

Following the soldiers wasn't difficult. They left deep boot prints in the mud on the dike embankments that filled up with rainwater. Karen and Sanger's biggest concern was that they were walking in enemy territory without any protection. The Viet Cong rarely took the time to distinguish between a soldier and a civilian. They followed a "shoot first, ask questions later" tradition. Karen and Sanger didn't stop to rest even though both of them were tired. Safety was a higher priority than sore muscles.

After twenty minutes of hiking on their own, they

spotted a soldier standing on a distant embankment. They waved and shouted to catch his attention. Spotting them he turned, took a hard look, leveled his rifle, and fired. Karen and Sanger hit the ground and crawled to the opposite side of a rice paddy embankment. "What the hell is he doing?" said Karen.

"He's VC," said Sanger. "Probably following the US soldiers."

"Oh, fuck."

"Yeah. Oh, fuck."

"What do we do?"

"How the hell am I supposed to know?"

"You've got more experience with this kind of thing."

"What? Getting shot at?"

"Well, yeah."

"We gotta move. He and his buddies will be coming to investigate."

"Okay. Where do we go?"

"Any place but here."

"There's a grove of trees over there," she said pointing.

"That's a long way, but let's give it a shot."

They moved through the rice paddies toward the clump of trees. Karen turned back and saw five Viet Cong soldiers closing on them. "God, I hope they're not rapey," said Karen.

"They're probably more interested in capturing us and collecting a reward than raping you," said Sanger.

As they drew closer to the woods, the Viet Cong closed the gap. It was going to be close and even if they reached the trees there wasn't much they could do. The VC fired at them. The bullets zinged past them, kicking up spats of mud when they hit the embankment in front of them. They made it to the trees and hid behind a fallen tree trunk. Karen reached into her rucksack and pulled out her pistol sealed in a plastic bag to keep it away from moisture. She removed the revolver from the bag. "Are you sure you wanna do that?" said Sanger.

"Do you think our press credentials are gonna protect us?"

"No. Maybe you should give it to me."

"Fuck off, Jerry."

Karen took aim and fired three rounds at the VC closing on their position. It had the desired effect. The VC dove into the rice paddy's muddy water. They returned fire but didn't advance... for the moment. "How much ammunition do you have?" said Sanger.

"Not enough. There's three more in the revolver and twelve more in a plastic bag in my rucksack," said Karen.

"I'll get 'em," said Sanger digging through her rucksack.

Karen took aim and fired another three rounds. She wasn't trying to kill anyone. She just wanted the VC soldiers to keep their heads down and stay away. Two of the VC started moving toward the far side of the trees as if they were going to try a flanking move. "We're gonna need a better plan," said Karen reloading.

"I'll be right back," said Sanger crawling off deeper into the trees.

Karen reloaded her pistol and waited another thirty seconds before firing off another three rounds. She was feeling very exposed without Sanger and his extra set of eyes. The two VC that were attempting to flank her had disappeared over the embankment. She knew they'd be coming soon. She tried to remain calm and stay focused. It wasn't easy. She heard footsteps behind her and said, "Jerry, is that you?"

The number of footfalls increased, and she knew it wasn't Jerry. She quickly pulled out the spent cartridges in her pistol and slid in new bullets in preparation for a firefight. More fired bullets from the VC in the rice paddy zinged into the trees. She turned to see they were once again advancing on her position. She fired three shots at them, hoping to buy more time. She was running out of options and felt cornered. She turned back to the trees and saw multiple shadows moving. She prepared to fire when rifle fire exploded from soldiers hidden behind trees. But the bullet flew past her and hit one of the VC in the rice paddy. He fell backward, one of his sandals slipping from his foot. His comrades grabbed him by the arms and pulled him through the water away from Karen. When she turned back, she saw American soldiers emerging from the woods and firing at the fleeing VC, then Sanger appeared and said, "Look who I found!"

"There're more in the woods," said Karen pointing in the direction of the VC that were flanking her.

A platoon lieutenant ordered a squad to search out the VC. The rest of his men chased after the VC in the rice paddy. "Sorry about leaving you in a lurch," said the lieutenant. "I didn't know we had left you behind. Some of my men can be real knuckleheads."

"All is forgiven if you've got an extra pair of boots. I don't care about size," said Karen.

"I can ask my guys, but I doubt it. We have enough stuff we gotta carry without an extra pair of boots."

Karen looked over at the VC sandal floating in the rice paddy. She waded out and retrieved it. Once on land, she saw that it was for the wrong foot, but put it on anyway. It was better than nothing.

The platoon radioman sent in a request for a pair of boots in Karen's size on the next supply run.

When the platoon reunited with C Company, the company commander, Captain Bill Carpenter stood on a dike holding up a pair of boots and said, "Who in the hell lost their boots on patrol?"

"That would be me, Captain," said Karen raising her hand.

"Well, shit. That explains the small size. You know, those choppers are for ammo and supplies. They're not your personal delivery service. Quartermaster said it was an emergency."

"Trust me, it is," said Karen as she grabbed the boots and sat down on the ground. Even with the VC sandal protecting her foot, her sock was worn through and bloody. She pulled off her boot and sandal, then socks. She flung the sandal into the rice paddy like a Frisbee. Next, she pulled two pairs of dry socks from her rucksack and doubled up to prevent the blisters she was sure would come as she broke in the boots. They were the only dry socks she had which meant that her feet would probably begin to rot before returning to the base. It didn't matter, she was grateful to have them and didn't dare ask for another pair.

"Are you gonna be okay?" asked the captain. "We can't have any lollygagging. This is a combat mission."

"I'll be fine. Thanks for the boots."

"U.S. tax dollars at work."

"Then God bless America."

"Hooah," said Carpenter and moved off.

The ARVN garrison at Tu Mo Rong had been surrounded by the NVA 24th Regiment and was being battered by communist heavy mortars. The ARVN 42nd Regiment was sent by road from Dak To to relieve the besieged garrison. 1st Battalion, 327th Infantry Regiment, 101st Airborne Division was flown by helicopter to set up blocking positions to the north and east of the garrison in hopes of catching the NVA when they retreated from their siege ring.

Hearing reports of the American troop movements, the NVA commander recognized the trap that was being set. While he did not want to give up his prize – the garrison, he also didn't want to turn a victory into a defeat. He prepared to move his men before they were surrounded by the superior allied force.

As the ARVN forces drew closer, the NVA forces packed up their mortars and withdrew. They would fight another day when the circumstances were more in their favor. On June 6th, the garrison at Tu Mo Rong was relieved. While the ARVN 42nd Regiment moved off to another position, the 1/327th and Company A 2nd Battalion, 502nd Infantry Regiment and Battery B 2nd Battalion, 320th Artillery Regiment took up positions within the relieved garrison and the surrounding area.

The next day at 2 AM, an NVA battalion from the 24th Regiment assaulted the positions of A Company, 2nd Battalion, 502nd Regiment, and B Company, 2nd Battalion, 320th Regiment near Dak Pha. Even though the first assault was driven back by the Americans, the NVA were tenacious and assaulted the Americans two more times before being driven from the battlefield by American air and artillery support. For the NVA it was a matter of honor not to leave a battlefield until an all-out effort to destroy the enemy had been made. It cost them heavy casualties but kept morale high. The NVA soldiers believed in their mission to reunite their homeland and drive the foreign armies out of their country.

Held in reserve until the battle lines solidified and the regiment commander could see where they were needed, the rest of 2nd Battalion, 502nd was committed to battle and dropped northeast of the battlefield. Karen and Jerry flew in on a supply helicopter after the initial landings. Jumping from the helicopter, Karen felt exhilarated and anxious. It was strange feeling both emotions at the same time. She wasn't sure which to trust. She knew her life would soon be in danger, but documenting the conflict was why she came to Vietnam. She couldn't do that from the safety of her hotel room. She realized there was no shame in feeling frightened as long she didn't stop her from doing her job. She snapped roll after roll of film as the action unfolded before her camera lens.

At 1 PM, Company A was drawn into a pitched battle with the NVA forces that lasted until nightfall. The communist losses were heavy when they finally withdrew.

The next afternoon, Company C, 2/502nd engaged an NVA battalion northwest of the garrison at Tu Mo Rong. Company B was maneuvering to assist C Company when it too was engaged by a different NVA battalion. The conflict took place in a bamboo thicket fifteen miles north of Dak To. At times, the fighting was hand-to-hand within the bamboo stalks.

Karen and Sanger were in the middle of the American troops that formed a protective wall. But the wall was crumbling as the Americans took losses and

Karen felt far from safe as she snapped photos of screaming North Vietnamese charging the American lines. C Company was in a bad position. They were trapped in a bowl that was surrounded by enemy troops on three sides and were being pounded by enemy mortars. As they closed in, the NVA were threatening to overrun the American position. Carpenter called in an airstrike.

When the aircraft armed with Napalm canisters arrived fifteen minutes later, Carpenter's position was already in the process of being overrun by the communists. He radioed the forward air controller circling above and said, "Lay it right on top of us. They're overrunning us, we might as well take some of them too."

Carpenter ordered his men to hunker down in preparation for the strike. Karen and Sanger were right in the middle of the battlefield. Karen saw the approaching aircraft. She knew it might be the last moments of her life. She raised her camera and started snapping photos of the approaching fighters.

Receiving instructions, two F-4C Phantom IIs released their canisters as they flew over the American position. The canisters tumbled through the air and landed bursting into a wall of flame. Snapping a last photo, Karen ducked and felt the intense heat as the flames rolled just a few yards from her and Sanger's position. The pain in her hands and the side of her face was severe. She turned away and tucked her hands under her body. She whimpered, then sobbed. She imagined her skin bubbling with blisters. It wasn't, but the fear was real.

When the heat dissipated, Karen looked up and saw a man engulfed in flames walking aimlessly in front of her. She couldn't tell if he was an American or North Vietnamese. After a few steps, he dropped to his knees, then finally fell to his side. He lay motionless. Karen was mortified at the sight and began shaking uncontrollably. Sanger wrapped his arms around her as she wept and said, "It's okay. He's done feeling pain."

When Karen recovered, she was never quite the same. She would often stare into the distance and remember the burning soldier. She wouldn't cry. She would just stare, emotionless, oblivious to her surroundings until something or someone snapped her out of her horrific daydream. It was sad that someone so young would carry such a burden for the rest of her life. She wasn't alone.

The napalm strike broke the NVA's assault. The communists disengaged and pulled back.

Captain Carpenter's controversial actions had saved most of his company. Some of his men died or were badly burned in the inferno. There were charred bodies strewn across the battlefield. It was a nauseating sight. Karen couldn't bring herself to take photos of the charred soldiers. It was the truth of war, but it seemed disrespectful.

During the relative calm, Company A linked up with C Company allowing the Americans to form an effective defensive perimeter that discouraged further enemy assaults. Air assaults and artillery barrages kept the NVA at bay until they finally withdrew. They had suffered enough.

The next day, 15 B-52s dropped 270 tons of bombs on NVA positions. The exploding bombs tore the earth, and anyone caught beneath them. The bombardment was more terrifying to the enemy than effective. Morale plummeted and many NVA ran from the battlefield.

Watching from a hillside after another B-52 airstrike in the valley below, the commander of 2/502nd said, "The strike devastated the area. The damage, in places, resembled that which could be expected from a low-yield nuclear weapon. The blowdown and cratering effect were enhanced by the use of 1000-pound bombs which seemed to have a significantly greater effect than the 750-pound bombs. This strike is considered the most effective strike ever exploited by this battalion. It is felt that the strike contributed significantly to the annihilation of the better part of an NVA battalion. Of special significance is the fact that the 2nd Battalion, 502nd Infantry suffered no friendly casualties subsequent to, and in the area of the strike."

The fierce fighting continued for several more days until all the NVA forces finally withdrew from the valley. A and C Companies had been badly battered and were withdrawn by helicopter to Dak To. Karen and Sanger were helelifted out with the last load of wounded. Karen took photos of the scared and blackened battlefield as the helicopter took off. She watched as a medic tended to a seriously wounded soldier that had been shot in the chest. She raised her camera and clicked off two photos. The medic looked over at her with disdain. She took a photo of his expression to remember the moment, then turned away as if uncaring. Sanger could see it. Karen was harder now. It made him gloomy like something had been taken from him.

American losses during Operation Hawthorne were forty-nine killed and 239 wounded, while the ARVN units had ten killed and twenty-nine wounded. The

North Vietnamese had 985 killed and twenty-one captured. The operation was supported by 445 tactical air assaults dropping 338 tons of ordinance. In addition, there were thirty-nine B-52 sorties that dropped an additional 702 tons of ordnance on the enemy. The Americans and South Vietnamese claimed victory since the NVA were driven from the area and suffered heavier losses. The operation also provided concrete evidence that the unplanned B-52 airstrikes used in a direct support role had been responsible for crumbling the enemy's resistance and ensuring an allied victory.

ALLIES

June 4, 1966 – Manilla, Philippines

By a vote of fifteen to eight, the Senate of the Philippines authorized President Ferdinand Marcos to send 2,000 soldiers to help fight the war in South Vietnam. The Filipino troops would join the forces of the United States, South Korea, Australia, and New Zealand in supporting South Vietnam's quest to defeat the Viet Cong and North Vietnamese invaders and thwart communist expansionism.

With each nation that joined the coalition, the United States looked less and less like an invading force themselves even though they provided the majority of troops and military aid to South Vietnam. The symbolism was not lost on the world press or at the United Nations.

June 29, 1966 – North Vietnam

The gloves were slowly coming off of the USAF and US Navy aviators as the White House and the Pentagon became more determined to demoralize the

North Vietnamese population. Sixteen U.S. Navy A-6 Intruders and twelve support aircraft launched from the aircraft carriers USS Ranger and USS Constellation. Their mission was to carry out the first American bombing of the largest cities in North Vietnam. They hit fuel and oil facilities near the city of Haiphong, North Vietnam's second largest city. Twenty-five minutes later twenty-five F-105 Thunderchiefs bombed fuel storage tanks in and around Hanoi.

Two months after the air assault, the CIA released a report that concluded that the heroic raids had escalated the war but failed to weaken public morale for which they had been designed. It seemed that whatever damage the American aircraft were able to inflict on their enemy, the North Vietnamese just bounced back within weeks, and sometimes days or even hours. Nothing could stop the Ant Army Ho Chi Minh had recruited to repair enemy damage wherever it occurred.

June 30, 1966 – Fort Hood, Texas, USA

Dissent against the war in Vietnam was growing in the United States and even in the ranks of the military. While the majority of Americans still supported the war, many were questioning the United States' commitment to fighting a protracted war so far from their nation's shores.

Things had reached a boiling point at Fort Hood, home of the III Armored Corps, First Army Division West, 1st Cavalry Division, and 3rd Cavalry Regiment. It was a huge military base with 158,706 acres of wide-open land and billeting for 6,007 officers and 82,610 enlisted personnel. Fort Hood was the largest U.S.

military installation in the world.

As a form of resistance to the war effort, three U.S. Army soldiers stationed at Fort Hood – Private First-Class James Johnson Jr., Private David Samas, and Private Dennis Mora publicly refused to deploy to Vietnam. It was one of the earliest acts of protest against the war in the U.S. military. To make their point of view known, the three soldiers filed suit against Secretary of Defense Robert McNamara and Secretary of the Army Stanley Resor to prevent their shipment to Vietnam. The three soldiers were in the 142nd Signal Company, 2nd Armored Division, and had working-class backgrounds. When the three found out that they were to be sent to Vietnam, they prepared a joint statement which was read during a press conference in New York City. It read in part:

"We represent in our backgrounds a cross-section of the Army and of America. James Johnson is a Negro, David Samas is of Lithuanian and Italian parents, and Dennis Mora is a Puerto Rican. We speak as American soldiers. We have been in the army long enough to know that we are not the only G.I.s who feel as we do. Large numbers of men in the service either do not understand this war or are against it... We know that Negroes and Puerto Ricans are being drafted and end up in the worst of the fighting all out of proportion to their numbers in the population; and we have firsthand knowledge that these are the ones who have been deprived of decent education and jobs at home... We have made our decision. We will not be a part of this unjust, immoral, and illegal war. We want no part of a war of extermination. We oppose the criminal waste of American lives and resources. We refuse to go to Vietnam!"

Mora, a Puerto Rican from Spanish Harlem and the most politically active of the three, also read his own statement which read in part:

"Contrary to what the Pentagon believes, cannon-fodder can talk. It is saying that we are not fighting for "freedom" in South Vietnam but supporting a Hitler-loving dictator. It is saying that it will not accept as a rationale for exterminating a whole people, theories of dominoes, Chinese "aggression" or arguments of "appeasement." It further says that the only foreign power in Vietnam today is the United States and that the Vietcong is an indigenous force which has the support of most of the people and is in control of eighty percent of the country."

Johnson, an African American from the Bronx, tied his antiwar stance to the racial discrimination he saw at home in the United States and said, "When the Negro soldier returns, he still will not be able to ride in Mississippi or walk down a certain street in Alabama. Just as the Negroes are fighting for absolute freedom and self-determination in the United States, so it is with the Vietnamese in their struggle against the Americans."

Many of the points the three soldiers had made were factually incorrect and reinforced some of the erroneous myths about the war. It didn't seem to matter to the three soldiers. They had the public's attention and were going to exploit it as much as possible.

One week after making their public statements in New York, the Three were scheduled to speak again to their supporters. Almost 800 people had turned up to hear them speak. On their way to the event, Samas, Mora, and Johnson were arrested by the U.S. Army military police.

Public protests did not stop as hundreds gathered outside the military prison where The Three were being held. Peter Seeger, the folk singer, and social activist wrote a song called the Ballad of the Fort Hood Three. It included the lines:

Come all you brave Americans and listen unto me,
If you can spare five minutes in this 20th century,
I'll sing to you a story true as you will plainly see
It's about three U.S. soldiers they call the "Fort Hood Three."

We've been told in training that in Vietnam we must fight;
And we may have to kill women and children, and that is quite all right;
We say this war's illegal, immoral, and unjust;
We're taking legal action, just the three of us.

We'll report for duty, but we won't go overseas.
We're prepared to face court martial, but we won't fight for Ky.
We three have talked it over, our decision now is clear,
We will not go to Vietnam, we'll fight for freedom here.

The Three were eventually charged with insubordination for refusing to board an aircraft that would carry them to Vietnam. They faced court-martial and were held under administrative restriction at Fort Dix in New Jersey. The court-martial proceedings took place in September 1966 over a three-day period. The defendants argued that the war was immoral and illegal. The presiding Army law officer dismissed their argument when he said, "I rule that it is a matter of law, that the war in Vietnam is legal, and I forbid you to argue that it isn't."

The military court convicted The Three of insubordination and sentence them to hard labor – Mora for three years while Samas and Johnson received five years each. Their appeal was denied, they were dishonorably discharged, and their pay was forfeited during their incarceration. Samas and Johnson later had their sentences reduced to three years by a military review board.

The Three also lost in Federal Court when a federal district judge cut off The Three's attorney, Stanley Faulkner, mid-argument and threw the case out. The judge read from a prepared opinion and said, "It is not the function of the judiciary to entertain such litigation which challenges the validity, the wisdom or the propriety of the Commander in Chief of our armed forces."

The actions of The Fort Hood Three became a turning point in the broader antiwar movement. It was the start of a rank-and-file protest against military authority and the war. It led to thousands of GIs against the war joining the resistance, many after having served honorably in Vietnam.

July 6, 1966 – Hanoi, North Vietnam

Shortly before the two-year anniversary of the Gulf of Tonkin Incident, the government of North Vietnam carried out the "Hanoi March" to call international attention to what it considered the illegal bombing of the north by the United States. In the previous months before the march, the politburo had suggested that the American prisoners, most of whom were captured airmen, might be tried for war crimes. The march of the POWs was designed to demonstrate the North Vietnamese anger from the bombing campaigns.

On July 6th, thirty-six POWs were herded by guards from the prison camp at Cu Loc nicknamed "The Zoo," and sixteen from the Xom Ap Lo prison camp called the "Briar Patch." Both groups were transported by truck to Hang Day Stadium in central Hanoi. Upon arrival, the POWs were issued uniforms stenciled with non-consecutive three-digit numbers that were designed to suggest that the North Vietnamese had far more prisoners than they did. Fewer than a hundred U.S. soldiers and aircrews had been captured by that time in the war. Many of the prisoners had spent months or even years in solitary confinement. The outing gave them a rare opportunity to see their fellow servicemen and greatly boosted their morale. Talking was expressly forbidden, so the prisoners communicated using a tap code they had developed. They shared their names, location, and other information.

When they arrived at the stadium, their interrogator known as "Rabbit" told the POWs they were about to meet the North Vietnamese people they had been bombing. The prisoners were shackled in pairs and marched down an avenue lined with tens of thousands of angry Vietnamese civilians. As the march continued, the crowd assaulted the American prisoners. Many of the Americans feared that their North Vietnamese captors had lost control of the crowd and thought they might be ripped to shreds by the mob. The Air Force pilot, Charles Boyd, who had been shot down near Hanoi, recalled, "Very shortly the parade got ugly. The organizers had obviously wanted to get the crowd riled up, angry, and even more committed to the war effort, but had no intention of turning the locals loose to maul, and ultimately kill the prisoners. They probably thought one guard per prisoner was enough to hold the crowd at bay. As the evening wore on it was clear that the prisoner/guard ratio was not enough."

The North Vietnamese guards continued to march the Americans for two miles as the event had degenerated into a riot. The North Vietnamese political officers feared for the Americans' safety and realized they would be held responsible for any unintended deaths. The POWs were returned to the stadium where the angry crowd waited for them. The shackled pairs of POWs had no choice but to fight their way into the interior of the stadium where they were finally safe from the mob. Later, they were returned to their assigned prisons.

International photojournalists and film crews had been brought in to witness the march. Their subsequent reports and images of American prisoners being assaulted by a mob brought considerable criticism of the North Vietnamese treatment of the Americans. UN Secretary-General U Thant denounced the North Vietnamese and their mistreatment of prisoners. India's Indira Gandhi and the United Kingdom's Harold Wilson urged the Soviet Union to rein in the North Vietnamese by threatening to cut off aid if the mistreatment of prisoners continued.

The North Vietnamese had achieved their goal of attracting international attention, but it wasn't what they had expected or desired. The members of the North Vietnamese politburo walked back their pledges to put the Americans on trial for war crimes and no such trials ever occurred. In the end, the public relations fiasco of the Hanoi March saved the American airmen's lives.

August 18, 1966 – Long Tan, South Vietnam

The Australian military had been advising and fighting in Vietnam since 1962 and their troop commitment increased as the war escalated. While initially attached to the US 173rd Airborne Brigade, along with the New Zealand Army artillery battery, the Australians had a unique manner of fighting and the Americans agreed that Australian combat forces should be deployed in their own area of operation. Independent from US forces, the Australians would be allowed to fight their own tactical war.

In April 1966, the 1st Australian Task Force (1 ATF) established its new base at Nui Dat in Phuoc Tuy Province. Consisting of two infantry battalions and a detachment from Special Air Service Regiment, 1 AFT was accompanied by a troop of M113 armored personnel carriers from the 4th/19th Prince of Wales Light Horse. The Australian also had their own helicopter and aircraft squadrons based out of Vung Tau Air Base and Phan Rang Air Base. 1 AFT's mission was to secure the countryside within the province while excluding larger towns that fell under American command.

Australian signals intelligence (SIGINT) had been tracking VC 275th Regiment and VC D445 Battalion through radio intercepts and sightings as they moved into position to the north of Long Tan, a village surrounded by a series of rubber plantations near Ba Ria, the provincial capital. The VC were just outside the range of the Australian artillery at Nui Dat.

The Viet Cong had established their dominion over the province and weren't willing to surrender it to the Australians without a fight. The VC leaders decided that a major defeat, like the Viet Minh had delivered to the French at Dien Bien Phu, would be politically unacceptable to civilians back in Australia who would demand their troops be brought home.

The Australian commander sent out patrols every morning and evening to clear the seven and a half-mile perimeter around the base. In addition, he had standing patrols outside the wire that would act as an early warning system if the Viet Cong attacked. Lastly, platoons were sent out to patrol and set up ambushes for any Viet Cong mortar teams within range of the compound. All civilians in the villages of Long Phuoc and Long Hai were removed and resettled nearby. The Australians were taking defensive measures further than the Americans by attempting to deny the Viet Cong from even observing their base. But the resettlement of villagers caused major resentment and pushed some civilians to support the Viet Cong cause.

The Viet Cong were still able to observe the Australian base from the hills surrounding Nui Dinh. The Viet Cong also sent sappers under the cover of darkness and heavy rain to locate Australian defenses. Under the command of Senior Colonel Nguyen The Truyen, the communists' main forces were the 274th and 275th Regiments of the 5th Division. The communist forces were comprised of Viet Cong guerrillas and regular NVA troops. The troops in 274th

Regiment were better trained and stronger with a total of 2,000 soldiers spread evenly over three battalions. The 275th also had three battalions but only totaled 1,850 troops. A heavy weapons battalion with 75 mm recoilless rifles, 82 mm mortars, and 12.7 mm heavy machine guns supported the two regiments. They were also supported by an engineer battalion, a signals battalion, a sapper reconnaissance battalion, plus logistic and medical units. Many of the troops had been recruited from the local area and had an intimate knowledge of the territory and villages. The division headquarters were located in the May Tao Mountains where it was out of range of allied artillery and hidden from aerial reconnaissance. Total communist strength was around 4,500 soldiers.

The backbone of the ARVN forces was the 52nd Ranger Battalion, a highly decorated unit that had defeated the NVA 275th Regiment the previous year. They were supported by seventeen Regional Force companies and forty-seven Popular Force platoons. The ARVN had a total force of about 4,500 although many of the Regional and Popular units were relatively weak and poorly trained.

1 ATF was under the command of Brigadier Oliver Jackson and two infantry battalions: the 5th Battalion under the command of Lieutenant Colonel John Warr and 6 RAR commanded by Lieutenant Colonel Colin Townsend. With all its supporting units, 1 AFT was the largest deployed Australian Task Force since World War II. Many of its officers and non-commissioned personnel had extensive operational experience. However, the force also had a large number of untrained National Servicemen within its ranks.

SAS teams carried out long-range patrols at the edge

of the Tactical Area of Operations searching for concentrations of enemy forces. 1 ATF commanders believed the VC were sure to respond as their freedom of action was curtailed by the Australian patrols. They expected the enemy to assault isolated companies or battalions rather than the entire Australian force at Nui Dat. The commanders also considered it likely that the enemy would try to cut off resupply convoys from Vung Tau. In July, there had been a number of violent skirmishes between the communists and the Australians.

At the end of July, Australian SIGINT used direction-finding equipment to track a VC radio transmitter belonging to the 275th Regiment as it moved closer to Nui Dat. The enemy was coming in force. The NVA 274th Regiment was nine miles northwest positioned next to Route 2. Their mission was to ambush a squadron of APCs from the US 11th Armored Cavalry Regiment that was sure to come from Long Khanh once the main battle had begun.

On August 17th at 2:43 AM, the communists began a bombardment against Nui Dat. Over 100 rounds from 82 mm mortars, 75 mm recoilless rifles, and an old 70 mm Japanese howitzer pounded the Australian positions killing one soldier and wounding another twenty-three. Most of the Australian infantry units were deployed outside the camp's perimeter at the time on patrols and ambushes. The Australians returned fire to the south and southeast where they suspected the mortars were located. The Australian artillery fired 240 rounds until the enemy mortars were silenced. The entire exchange lasted twenty-two minutes. Expecting an enemy ground assault, the Australians remained alert. The enemy attack never came. The Viet Cong and

NVA were gone.

As dawn approached, Townsend ordered B Company, 6 RAR under the command of Major Noel Ford to locate the enemy firing positions and ensure that they were indeed abandoned. A platoon from Company C mounted APCs and moved to patrol in the opposite direction. Even more, patrols were sent out in all directions to find the enemy and its mortars. With much of 6 RAR's troops out on patrol, Jackson felt the garrison would be shorthanded if the enemy chose to attack. He called back 5 RAR which was expected to arrive at Nui Dat by August 18th.

Patrolling at the edge of a rubber plantation, the Australians discovered several heavy weapons and mortar pits. Abandoned pieces of uniforms with large blood stains revealed the accuracy of the Australian's artillery.

On the 18th, more Australian patrols were sent out to locate the enemy, who most believed had already left the area. D Company was sent out to relieve B Company who was scheduled for leave that afternoon. The rock and roll entertainers Little Pattie and Col Joye and the Joy Boys had been flown in to entertain the Australians with an afternoon concert at Nui Dat. Many of the Australian troops out on patrol were disappointed that they would miss the performance. Even at a distance, they could hear the music through the trees and echoing off the hills.

A mile and a half from Nui Dat, D Company linked up with B Company at the edge of the Long Tan rubber plantation. The plantation had thousands of trees spaced an equal distance apart. The leaves formed a thick canopy that prevented aerial identification of any soldiers moving through the plantation, friend or foe. The trees also prevented any landing of a helicopter within the plantation.

Major Harry Smith, the commander of D Company decided to continue the pursuit of the enemy on a new trail with fresh sandal prints leading to the northeast. The company was spread out with the men being positioned twenty yards apart, a larger spacing than adopted by US and ARVN units. Platoons 10 and 11 took the lead advancing side-by-side while the headquarters platoon followed in the middle and Platoon 12 followed as a rear guard. The formation allowed them to cover a broad front but with little flanking security.

At 3:40 PM, 10 and 11 Platoons entered a tree line as a VC squad walked out of the tree line and into the middle of the headquarters platoon. Their eyes adjusting to the sunlight, the VC did not notice the Australians on both sides. Platoon Sergeant Bob Buick raised his assault rifle and fired killing one VC soldier and startling the rest. The VC scattered keeping low in the elephant grass. Buick could not fire again without the risk of hitting his own men in the crossfire. He had no choice but to allow the VC soldiers to escape. The Australians wrote off the encounter as a fleeting contact and not part of the main enemy body. Smith radioed the task force headquarters and reported the brief engagement.

With the area clear of the initial contact, Smith ordered D Company to continue their advance to the east. Under the command of Second Lieutenant Gordon Sharp, 11 Platoon had moved out quicker than the other platoons and opened up a 550-yard gap between themselves and the headquarters platoon. Penetrating further into the rubber plantation in search of the VC squad, 11 Platoon veered off between the rubber trees opening a 300-yard gap with 10 Platoon. The two flanking platoons had lost sight of each other. In addition, the Australian platoons had now moved apart so much that the platoons were outside the effective range of their assault rifles covering each other.

At 4:08 PM, 11 Platoon's left flank came under enemy machine-gun fire from an undetected VC force. Several Australians were hit with two being killed. The Australians went to ground firing from prone positions just as a second enemy machine gun opened fire from a different direction. Tracer round zipped over the Australians' heads. The firing lasted three minutes and then suddenly stopped. Sharp ordered the rest of the platoon to sweep in front of the pinned soldiers. As the platoon moved forward, they came under small arms and RPG fire from their front and both flanks. The Australian platoon was surrounded on three sides with little to no cover and under threat of being overrun. The men in the isolated platoon were forced to fight for their lives as they attempted to buy time for the rest of D Company to reach them. Pinned down by the heavy fire, Platoon 11 had run into the front lines of the main force of the enemy regiment. Bugle calls resounded as elements of the VC regiment maneuvered to encircle the Australian platoon and destroy it.

New Zealand artillery forward observer Captain Maurice Stanley heard the reports of the encircled platoon and wasted no time bringing 161st Battery, Royal New Zealand Artillery into action. Although he could not see the Australian platoon, Stanley knew their last reported position. He directed the initial rounds 300 yards from that location and allowed the platoon radio operator to guide the rounds closer without hitting the platoon. Because of the platoon's position between the New Zealand battery and the VC regiment in front of them, the rounds passed over their heads and exploded deep in the VC's lines. With a few more shells the radio operator was able to walk in the rounds so they were landing on the VC directly in front of the platoon and on their flanks. Once he had the artillery dialed in, Stanley requested a regimental fire mission using all twenty-four guns of the 1st Field Regiment. Shells rained down on the Viet Cong and NVA troops, exploding and sending hot shrapnel in all directions. But the enemy troops were well disciplined and didn't break. They continued to maneuver around the Australian platoon that had already suffered more than thirty percent casualties of dead and wounded. The rain was falling so heavy that neither side had a good view of their opponent and that made the VC cautious. They didn't know how many enemy soldiers they were fighting.

Seeing D Company approaching, the VC fired 60 mm mortar rounds at them driving them to the ground and slowing their progress. D Company moved behind a small hill that offered them some protection against the enemy's machine-gun fire. Allied artillery strikes were called in to silence the VC mortars and allow D Company to continue its rescue of the isolated platoon.

Hearing the artillery shriek overhead and explode on his flank, Sharp raised his head to spot the artillery hits and adjust fire. A Viet Cong rifle bullet hit Sharp in the forehead. His body went limp, and he died.

Seeing his platoon commander dead, Buick took charge of 11 Platoon. The platoon continued to take heavy casualties and was running dangerously low on ammunition. Buick radioed Smith for further assistance, but as he did his radio's antenna was shot off and communications were lost.

Smith realized that 11 Platoon wouldn't last long on their own. He ordered Kendall's 10 Platoon to wheel around to the southeast and advance to the left flank of 11 Platoon only two hundred yards away and relieve some of the pressure from enemy fire.

Dropping their packs and filling their pockets with as much ammunition as they could hold, Kendall and his platoon crested the small hill between the two platoons and saw a VC platoon through the heavy rain closing on 11 Platoon's position. Kendall ordered his men to hold fire as they silently moved up behind the VC platoon. They dropped to their knees, aimed, and fired into the back of the VC platoon killing a dozen enemy soldiers. The surprise assault broke the VC attack as they retreated dragging their dead and wounded with them.

Hoping to take advantage of the lull as the enemy retreated, Kendall ordered his men forward.

Closing to within 100 yards of 11 Platoon's position, 10 Platoon came under heavy fire from three sides and were forced to the ground. The Australians of 10 Platoon crawled into a defensive circle and fought to hold on. Kendall radioed for reinforcements when his radio was hit by a bullet, and he too lost communications. He immediately sent a runner to find another radio and bring it back to the platoon. With the runner gone, Kendall knew that at the very least his platoon was relieving some of the pressure on 11 Platoon.

Ten minutes later, the runner returned with the

spare radio, and Kendall reestablished communication with Smith. To Kendall's disappointment, Smith ordered 10 Platoon to pull back under the cover of artillery. Kendall wanted to argue that his men could reach 11 Platoon if given proper support, but he knew that it was not the time. He obeyed Smith's order and 10 Platoon retreated back to the point where they had started.

It appeared that 11 Platoon was lost and the VC would shortly overrun their position. No quick reaction force had been organized before the fighting began and it would take time to cobble one together. VC radio jamming broke communications with 11 Platoon until they found another channel on which to communicate with headquarters. The messages back and forth needed to be short because it wouldn't take long before the Viet Cong found the new radio channel and jammed it once again. It was one of the things that concerned Jackson. Such radio jamming methods were usually only seen at a VNA division level. That meant that Jackson's task force was facing a much larger enemy force than originally suspected.

Townsend was determined not to lose 11 Platoon. He personally took charge of the relief force which would be made up of A Company, 3 Troop 1st APC Squadron, and B Company. In addition, Bien Hoa Air Base was put on alert for air support. When Townsend telephoned Jackson for final permission to lead the rescue force, Jackson was reluctant to allow such a large force to leave Nui Dat, which he believed was under threat of being attacked by an entire communist division. Townsend reminded Jackson that the US II FFV could be called upon if the communist attack was substantial. While Jackson agreed to generally support the rescue mission, he would not release the required force until absolutely necessary. He was cautious and believed he would need the bulk of his forces if Nui Dat was attacked. Townsend was beyond frustrated but his hands were tied for the moment. He believed that Jackson's hesitation could cost the lives of the men in 11 Platoon.

Smith believed D Company was at the very least facing a communist battalion and probably more. His platoons were spread out too far and unable to support each other. The artillery battery supporting his company was forced to fire around the individual platoons instead of consolidating its fire around the entire company position. Smith planned on pulling the entire company into one defensive position where air and artillery could support his men more effectively.

The VC were probing the Australian company's flanks but had difficulty finding the end of their lines because the individual Australian soldiers were dispersed over a wider area than the South Vietnamese and US companies that they were used to fighting. The communist commander overestimated the size of the force he was fighting and became over-cautious.

Knowing that 11 Platoon would likely be overrun and wiped out in the next few minutes. Buick had established communications with Stanley. Buick could see that VC were massing on an assault line in front of his position. Only ten of the twenty-eight men in 11 Platoon could still fight and they were almost completely out of ammunition. Buick had little hope that he and his men would survive another ten minutes. He asked Stanley to fire on his own position once the enemy's final assault started. Stanley refused even though he recognized 11 Platoon's precarious situation. Instead, he nailed down what he believed was Buick's exact position and agreed to fire much closer to what was left of 11 Platoon's defense line.

A few minutes later, as the VC rose to begin their final assault, New Zealand artillery shells rained down just 160 feet in front of 11 Platoon's positions. As the VC advanced, their entire assault line was wiped out by red-hot shrapnel and compression from the thunderous explosions. The artillery saved Buick and his platoon for the moment. Three US F-4 Phantoms arrive on station. The fighter aircraft bombed and Napalmed the VC assault survivors as they retreated racking up the body count and giving the VC commanders pause. Dozens of enemy bodies were strewn in front of 11 Platoon's position.

A few minutes later, Smith radioed in that D Company was running low on ammunition and needed an aerial resupply. Because of the dense trees within the plantation, helicopters would be unable to land. The ammunition boxes would need to be dropped through the trees making it unpredictable where they would land. Smith chose a drop sight 400 yards west of his position to ensure none of his men were hurt by the falling crates. Unfortunately, the trees and enemy fire made it impossible for the helicopters to take D Company's wounded. The wooden ammunition crates were wrapped in blankets for the wounded and to protect the boxes as they landed.

Just as two Iroquois helicopters made the drop in heavy rain and under enemy fire, the VC began an assault against D Company's position. Allied fighter aircraft were stacked up and ready to assist, but the artillery needed to be halted before they could fly into the immediate area around D Company. It was a gamble giving the VC a lull in artillery fire as they charged the Australian's front line. Smith took the risk, called off the artillery, and called in the fighters.

The Phantom fighters dropped their Napalm canisters on top of the waves of charging VC. A wall of fire rose up in front of D Company's position and when it calmed the charging VC were gone. Only dozens of burning bodies remained. Their guns empty, the Australians wasted no time in retrieving the ammunition dropped by the helicopters. Smith called for the aircraft to clear the area so he could resume artillery support. After a few minutes, artillery shells once again bombarded the VC positions keeping the enemy from making another attempt to overrun D Company's position.

Smith ordered 12 Platoon to attempt to link up with 11 Platoon on their right flank. Smith knew it was a long shot because of the VC's numerical superiority but he wasn't willing to give up on saving 11 Platoon. 12 Platoon performed a button-hook style maneuver to end up on 11 Platoon's flank, but it was still over 150 yards away from 11 Platoon's position when the VC gunfire and mortar shells drove them to the ground. With his entire company pinned down, Smith requested an airmobile assault but because of bad weather and no place to land through the trees, he was told it was impossible. Instead, Townsend told Smith that an infantry company mounted in APCs would be deployed as a relief force. It would take time to get it all organized, but it was better than nothing.

When the APCs arrived at Nui Dat, Jackson once again intervened delaying their deployment to rescue D Company. Jackson wanted the APCs to defend the base from the attack he knew was coming. He felt that the attack on D Company was a feint to distract the Australians and split their forces even more. It took Townsend over an hour to convince Jackson to release the APCs and A Company that would ride with them to rescue D Company.

Meanwhile, 12 Platoon was attacked on three sides as the VC tried to cut off any rescue attempt for 11 Platoon. Fighting valiantly to hold their position near 11 Platoon, 12 Platoon was also in danger of being overrun and wiped out. As the rain intensified once again and visibility was cut to seventy-five yards, 12 Platoon lost sight of 11 Platoon and feared they had been overrun.

Buick and 11 Platoon had maintained their position under heavy enemy fire and multiple assaults for over two hours. Most of the men were either wounded or dead. Unknowing that 12 Platoon was nearby and had shifted some of the enemy fire away from his men, Buick decided to take advantage of a lull in the fighting. Following their sergeant, the men of 11 Platoon rose carrying their wounded and made a mad scramble to the west where he hoped to find D Company headquarters. Within seconds, 11 Platoon was hit by intense enemy fire as they made their dash. One soldier was killed and two more were wounded. Buick called out to identify his platoon where he thought the Australian headquarters were located. Instead, he saw yellow smoke marking a position. Desperate and under fire, he and his men moved toward it. It was 12 Platoon who was also heavily engaged with the enemy.

Deciding that staying in their current position would allow the VC to eventually overrun them, the two platoons made a wild run, fighting as they moved, back to D Company's position. It worked.

Once inside D Company's defensive perimeter, Smith quickly assigned the men in both platoons' positions around his defensive perimeter. With all his platoons now consolidated, Smith could call in air and artillery strikes without fear of hitting his own men. He radioed Stanley, gave him the news, and told him to let loose with everything he had. Stanley was only too happy to comply.

Artillery shells exploded in mass on the enemy positions around D Company chewing up the VC like a hungry bear, driving the enemy to the ground. For a moment, the VC broke contact with D Company allowing Smith the once again reorganize his men into a stronger fighting position and pass out ammunition to everyone that needed it. Smith walked around his perimeter checking on his men and getting a good look at the situation. Even though everyone had been battered by the enemy, morale remained surprisingly high now that 11 Platoon had been rescued. Smith figured the entire company was at sixty percent strength. They had created an aid station for the wounded, but it was pinning them down and keeping them from moving to a safer position closer to Nui Dat with its heavy machine guns and recoilless rifles.

Confused by the movements of the two platoons, the VC relocated the Australian's consolidated position and opened fire with their heavy machine guns. As the VC formed up for a massive assault, Stanley called in his artillery strikes. When the VC rose from their protected positions, they were met with a very accurate artillery strike that wiped out the second attack wave used as a reserve by the VC. The front assault force advanced 100 yards before they realized that their reserve was not following them. More shells exploded around them. Pulling back seemed no safer than moving forward. They chose neither and went to ground among their wounded and dead. From prone positions, the VC riflemen could accurately fire on the Australians on the ridge of the hill firing down on them. Many of the Australians were hit in the head and chest, killing several and wounding even more.

While the Australians in D Company were clearly outnumbered by the VC, Stanley had done an outstanding job of calling accurate artillery strikes which held back the enemy assaults. If the VC attacked simultaneously with all their assault units, D Company would have most assuredly been overrun and destroyed. Confusion about the size of the Australian force had saved the company.

Unable to move because of their aid station filled with wounded, D Company's only hope was reinforcements from Nui Dat. To make matters worse, the heavy rain was causing flooding through the rubber plantation making it difficult for a relief force to reach D Company's position.

The VC continued to bring in fresh forces to attack the Australians and didn't seem overly concerned at the heavy cost they were paying in their soldiers' lives. They were determined to destroy D Company.

Lieutenant Adrian Roberts was in command of 3 Troop. With ten APCs loaded with 100 men from A Company, 3 Troop pressed forward from the South through the mud and rain dodging trees and occasionally running a few over. Intent on taking command of D Company, Townsend rode in one of the APCs. To reach D Company, 3 Troops needed to traverse the heavily swollen Suoi Da Bang, the creek running parallel to the rubber plantation. Using a bullock track alongside a dam, Roberts was able to ease the armored vehicles down the creek's steep embankment. Pushing forward as quickly as possible, he swam the carriers across the creek despite the threat of fast-flowing water.

Once on the other side of the creek, the APCs advanced another mile and came to a junction that would lead them directly into the battlefield where D Company was fighting for their lives. Roberts knew there was no time to spare if he and his men were going to rescue the besieged Australians. Roberts was unaware of D Company's exact location but could hear the heavy gunfire in the distance. He had his APCs form a battle line spacing them 40 yards apart and two rows deep. On his order, the armored line rapidly advanced toward the sound of battle.

As they moved through the plantation and with the heavy rain masking the noise of their engines, the troop of APCs encountered a VC battalion attempting to outflank D Company. Protected by thick gun shields, the vehicle commanders opened fire with their heavy machine guns as the rear doors were lowered and the soldiers of A Company poured out taking up a firing position that would protect the armored vehicles from flanking and rear enemy actions.

Initially surprised by the armored vehicles appearing through the trees, D445 Battalion scrambled for cover and returned fire. Raked by the APCs' heavy machine guns, the VC took substantial casualties. Disordered by the Australian attack, the VC were forced to abandon their encirclement of D Company and retreat to the east. In the space of just a few minutes, the VC had lost forty killed, while the Australians only had one wounded. It was a very lopsided battle.

With the Viet Cong withdrawing, Roberts ordered the infantry to climb back in the armored vehicles and for his rescue force to advance again. The deeper they traveled away from the creek and the deep water and mud, the faster the vehicles were able to move.

At the same time, 3 Troop was speeding toward the battlefield, B Company was also approaching on foot. In the heavy rain, the vehicle commanders saw soldiers moving toward D Company's position. Believing they were VC, the commanders opened fire on their own men. Although it only lasted a minute before the commander of B Company was able to radio the APCs, one soldier was seriously wounded.

As the newly combined rescue force advanced, they engaged a small group of VC from behind. An enemy 57 mm recoilless rifle fired at one of the APCs narrowly missing it and slamming into a nearby tree that was blown apart. The remains of the tree landed on top of the APC. A second recoilless rifle fired on the APC and hit the remains of the tree saving the APC and the crew inside. When his heavy machine gun jammed, the vehicle commander used his personal weapon, an Owen gun, to kill the VC three-man gun crew. After suffering heavy losses, the VC retreated back to their lines. The APCs and B Company continued to advance.

Roberts still did not know D Company's exact location but believed they were close. He ordered his men to check their fire for fear of again attacking the wrong soldiers in the heavy rain and dense trees. B Company engaged more VC attempting to attack the APCs from the rear. When some of the heavy machine guns on the APCs swung around and opened fire, the VC took heavy losses of forty-five killed.

Seeing the APCs appear through the trees and engage the enemy attacking them, the survivors of D Company stood and cheered. As the sun was setting, Townsend ordered Roberts to attack the flank of the VC's main lines. With Australian artillery dropping on the VC, Roberts ordered his vehicle commanders to button up as much as possible to protect the crews inside. The commanders of vehicles with gun shields remained behind their heavy machine guns and fired on the enemy as they once again advanced.

Having lost the majority of their recoilless rifle teams, the VC were unable to stop the APCs from flanking them. Australian artillery continued to pound the VC's firing positions taking their toll. Outgunned and outmaneuvered, the VC's fighting spirit was broken. They broke contact with the Australians and withdrew as the sunset. The APCs cleared the trees in front of D Company's position allowing the wounded to finally be evacuated and the survivors to be transported back to Nui Dat. D Company's fight was finally over. Battered and bloodied, Smith and his men had survived against insurmountable odds.

The Battle of Long Tan became a legend in Australian military history. The Australians had suffered eighteen killed and twenty-four wounded while the communists had 245 killed and 350 wounded. While both sides claimed victory, it was the Australians that remained at Nui Dat. The VC had failed to accomplish a strong political victory by racking up large enemy losses. The soldiers of the 1st Australian Task Force were cheered as heroes when they finally returned home. The day that the Battle of Long Tan was fought was to be observed annually by Australians and became known as Vietnam Veterans'

Remembrance Day.

BATON ROUGE

August 23, 1966 – Long Tau River, South Vietnam

Part of a fleet of 531 Victory ships, the SS Baton Rouge Victory was built during World War II as part of the Emergency Shipbuilding program – cheap cargo ships that could be built within fifty-five-days if needed. With improved hull designs, Victory ships were slightly larger and faster than Liberty ships which had been the backbone of the Navy's cargo transport effort. The Victory ships were armed with a five-inch stern gun for use against submarines and surface ships and a bow-mounted three-inch gun, plus eight 20 mm anti-aircraft cannons.

Like most of the Liberty and Victory ships, the Baton Rouge had been decommissioned after World War II and mothballed in the James River in case it was needed in the future. With the Vietnam War gaining momentum, the Baton Rouge was recommissioned as a federally owned merchant vessel sailed by Merchant Marines.

On July 28th, the SS Baton Rouge Victory set sail for San Francisco loaded with military trucks and tractors, automobiles, mail, and general cargo. It sailed for almost a month without incident on its way to Vietnam.

On August 26th, the ship entered the mouth of the Long Tau River, twenty-two miles southwest of Saigon. Using Soviet-made scuba gear, four Viet Cong commandos waited underwater in the channel as the ship approached. They were armed with two-magnetic 2,400-pound limpet mines floated underwater with neutral buoyancy devices. As the ship passed, the divers attached the limpet mines next to each other on the ship's hull. Once the mines were attached, the divers swam for their lives toward shore. Fearful of the compression wave, the saboteurs wanted to get out of the water before the mines detonated.

A few minutes later, the two mines exploded tearing a sixteen-by-forty-five-foot hole in the ship's hull and killing seven American civilian sailors. As the ship took on water, the number 3 cargo hold flooded completely, and the ship began to sink. Fearful that his sinking ship would block the shipping channel, the Baton Rouge's captain ran his vessel aground.

Four days later, the SS Baton Rouge Victory was refloated and towed to Vung Tau. Eventually, the heavily damaged ship was towed to Formosa and scrapped.

The attack on the SS Batton Rouge was the largest loss of life event due to enemy action on merchant mariners in the Vietnam War. The seven seamen that lost their lives were remembered at the American Merchant Seaman Memorial in San Francisco.

September 11, 1966 – South Vietnam

For the first time since the South Vietnamese military junta had taken over the government, the citizens were allowed to vote for elected officials. Despite the Viet Cong carrying out dozens of attacks on polling places across the country, eighty point eight percent of the 5,288.512 registered voters cast their ballots to elect members of a constituent assembly that was tasked with designing a new constitution for South Vietnam.

The Americans and other foreigners cheered the election as a step in the right direction. Their hope was that when allowed to choose their own destiny, the people of Vietnam would support the war against the communists.

Saigon, South Vietnam

After Operation Hawthorne, Karen had stuck to Saigon. Using the lame excuse that she had some weird stomach bug that wouldn't go away, she had turned down several embed assignments that were offered to her. She convinced herself that she just needed more time to adjust to what had happened. The strange part was that she had seen people burned alive before when she was in the United States covering anti-war protests. But those protestors had set themselves on fire willingly to protest the Vietnam War. Seeing a man consumed in flame during a battle was different somehow. She didn't know why. It just was. If she was being truly honest, it scared her. A few feet one way or another and it could have been her. She had nightmares and woke in a cold sweat gasping for breath. The imaginary flames having consumed all oxygen. The first thing she reached for was her hair. The thought of losing her hair terrified her more than anything. Once she felt that it was still there, she was able to calm herself and realized it was just a dream… a very bad dream.

She received a base salary from the Associated Press and therefore couldn't just turn down every assignment. She spent her time photographing social events and public relations photo ops. She knew the other photojournalist that had seen her photos considered it beneath her, but it was all she could do at the moment. She was an emotional wreck.

She was drinking more too. She used alcohol to calm her nerves. At least that was what she told herself. In reality, she was just bored. Bored in Saigon? Bored in a war zone?

She had become a bit of a tramp. She wasn't interested in a relationship, but sex kept her mind off things and helped her sleep. And why not? Saigon was full of American soldiers on leave with one thing on their mind and if they could sleep with an American woman, all the better. But when they asked when they could see her again, she was aloof and unsure when she would be back in Saigon. She figured she was going no harm. They had gotten what they wanted. She didn't need more… not from them.

She knew she had to get back out in the field, or she might as well pack her bag and go back to the states where it was safe. She hated the thought of giving up and going home to her mother. Her mother? That's what she needed. Her mother was smart as a whip and able to think things through better than she could do herself, especially with her mind the way it was, all mixed up and unable to focus.

The next day, she headed over to the Hotel Continental. Like many journalists she had her mail sent to Saigon's most popular hotel. She never knew where she was going to be, but the Continental would always be there. The manager of the hotel didn't mind. Most journalists were big drinkers and would usually visit the rooftop lounge or the patio bar and have a drink while sorting through and reading their mail. They usually ran into other journalists and could stay for hours in the middle of the day, drinking and eating. Mail was good business.

As expected, there were three letters from her mother, one of from her brother Scott, and plethora of bills, junk mail, and letters from friends and associates. Just as the manger had expected, she went to the patio bar, sat at a table under the awning and next to the street. It was dangerous place to sit before the hotel had greatly increased security. Viet Cong on motorbikes were known to toss grenades at the foreigners sitting on the patio as they passed by. Karen didn't care. She felt safe in Saigon. She ordered a Tom Collins, checked the postmark dates, and opened the first letter from her mother.

The letter consisted of asking a bunch of questions about her safety, her health, if she had met anyone interesting, and whether she was eating enough vegetables. Next came the update on what was happening at home and with the family. She had a big extended family that included everyone including third cousins and step aunts and uncles. Someone was always getting a divorce or pregnant, sometimes both. Weddings, graduations, and anyone that had been drafted or volunteered were next, then sickness, soldiers wounded in battle, and funerals. Finally, were homecomings, birthdays, and births. It only seemed logical, a little sugar, then a little salt, then back to sugar. Her mother, a schoolteacher, was very organized in everything she did including writing letters. Finally, her mother expressed her love. Karen teared up. It was just a stupid letter but exactly what she needed. Within moments, she was openly weeping. The waiter came over with her Tom Collins and asked if everything was okay. She nodded yes in between gasps of breath and wiping her nose and dapping her eyes with the neatly rolled cloth napkin on the table. She knew that no matter what she did, her mother would always be there ready to take her in even if she had no hair. She laughed at the stupidity of the thought.

It was on that patio, drinking a Tom Collins while reading the second letter from her mother that Karen decided to take the next opportunity offered to her to embed with a unit in the field. The thought both terrified and exhilarated her. She would fight her way back to the fearless photojournalist that she once was… even if it killed her.

Two days later, Karen was offered an assignment to embed with the 196th Light Infantry Brigade commanded by Brigadier General Edward de Saussure. She would be accompanied by Simon Bryant, an AP journalist with almost a decade of experience in Southeast Asia. She would need to move quickly as the brigade was moving out the next day where they would interdict the flow of arms to the Viet Cong around Saigon and the Mekong Delta. In so doing, the Americans hoped to engage the NVA and Viet Cong. She accepted and caught the first supply helicopter she could find to take her to the brigade's base in Tay Ninh province and meet up with Bryant.

The 196th Brigade had arrived in South Vietnam a

month earlier. Except for a few veteran officers and NCOs, the troops were fairly green. They had not seen major combat in Vietnam and their commander was also new. While De Saussure was considered by many to an excellent officer and an authority on missiles, he had never commanded infantry.

De Saussure kicked off Operation Attleboro with a series of battalion-sized sweeps of the area around the base. One battalion would go out on patrol while the other two battalions remained behind to finish the construction of the brigade's base camp.

Karen would go with whichever battalion was in the field at the time. Much of her time was spent finding her way through elephant grass with the rest of the patrol. The tiny teeth on the grass blades made annoying little cuts in her skin that would quickly become infected producing a yellow puss. Rolling out her sleeves helped, but then she would sweat profusely from the heat and humidity.

Moving through elephant grass was intimidating because it was tall and dense. At times, she couldn't see where she was stepping and lost sight of trail the soldiers in the unit had made. When she got separated from the patrol, she followed a sergeant's advice and didn't call out. There were Viet Cong in the area and if they found her first, her situation would be far worse. Instead, she would wait patiently until Bryant informed the unit commander that she was missing, and he would send a team to look for her. When they finally found her, it was an intense moment. She would hear someone approaching, but she didn't know if they were friend or enemy. She would hold her breath until the grass parted and an American face appeared.

The soldiers never scolded her. She wasn't

supposed to be an expert. They kept an eye on her and helped when she needed it. It was like having a bunch of big brothers. She took photos of everyone she met, so she would remember them and, at times, send a photo to a family if their son was lost in battle. She was never sure if it helped the families seeing a photo of their son in the field, but she decided to let them have the option and would send the photo. She thought about her brother, Scott, and if she would want a photo of him in his helicopter if he died. She would and she thought her mother would too.

Bryant and Karen would only stay with the patrol for a few days, then go back to Saigon to work on other assignments. They would return quickly when they received reports that the task force had contacted the enemy. The AP wasn't interested in non-productive sweeps by American troops. That story had been told over and over again. Most newspapers refused to pick up the AP's articles and photos unless there was some kind of action beyond troops slugging their way through rice paddies and elephant grass. It was the way of warfare in Vietnam – endless monotony interspersed with moments of terror. The public was more interested in the terror. It was a shameless promotion of violence and human tragedy, but it sold newspapers.

For two weeks, the Americans found nothing. They knew from intelligence reports that the Viet Cong were in the area, but for whatever reason they had chosen not to engage the Americans. It was frustrating for the troops in the brigade who were anxious to tangle with the enemy and prove their worth. No such luck.

When 25th Division discovered a large cache of rice

near the Saigon River, de Saussare and his brigade were ordered to search for additional rice stockpiles farther east. While hunting for rice storage was far from glamourous, it was better than beating the bushes around Tay Ninh which had been completely fruitless.

Within a week of scouring the new area with consisted of low, flat terrain and cultivated fields, a unit from the brigade stumbled upon a long row of sheds covered with black plastic. Inside the huts were tons of rice that could feed thousands of Viet Cong troops. In the days that followed, 196th Brigade found several larger caches of rice. Since none of the rice stockpiles were near a river or road, the rice had to be bagged, then airlifted by CH-47 helicopters with belly-slings. It was a time-consuming process for the soldiers in the brigade. After having packed up and transported 120 tons of rice, an intelligence unit in the brigade discovered an enemy document that mentioned more hidden stockpiles to the north and that the VC were in the process of organizing an area defense to protect the rice.

De Saussure and his men spent one more day shipping off as much rice as possible then burned the remaining 700 tons using dozens of Willie Pete phosphorous grenades and hundreds of gallons of gasoline brought in by helicopter. Free from rice duty, the brigade moved out toward Ba Hao, a stream emptying into the Saigon River five miles northwest of Dau Tieng.

When 1st Battalion, 27th Infantry Regiment, on loan for search operations, began their hunt for the rice stockpiles and the enemy troops guarding them, they once again came up empty-handed.

De Saussure decided to change tactics and up the

ante. With the base at Tay Ninh almost completed, he sent two battalions – 2nd Battalion, 1st Infantry Regiment and 4th Battalion, 31st Infantry Regiment – north over four separate jungle routes toward the Ba Hao. At the same time, he sent two companies from the 1/27th Infantry by helicopter to divergent blocking position south of the stream. With no link up plan, the four attacking columns and the two blocking forces remained separated from one another and became lost in the tall elephant grass and dense jungle that permeated the area. It was a bad beginning.

Shortly before noon, an NVA and Viet Cong force attacked one of the blocking forces through the elephant grass around them. The American commander was killed by shrapnel from an exploding enemy mortar shell and the company took heavy casualties. De Saussure sent two companies from his reserve force by helicopter to reinforce the company under attack. In addition, two companies from the attacking columns arrived and took up the fight.

Karen and Bryant received word of the firefight. "What do you think?" said Karen.

"I think if the fighting continues another day, this thing may build into a major battle," said Bryant.

"So, we go?"

"Yeah. We go."

Karen and Bryant pulled as many strings as they could to catch a ride on cargo plane heading into the area, then a helicopter carrying ammunition and supplies that took them close to the battlefield. From there they followed the ammunition until it reached the American forces under attack.

Karen and Bryant were surprised by the intensity of the battle and how quickly it had developed. The

Americans units were pinned down and had difficulty maneuvering. The area was filled with enemy mines and boobytraps that slowed the Americans and made them overly cautious. Enemy snipers hidden the jungle canopy took their toll on the American troops and their morale. The rescue forces had failed to turn the tide of battle in the Americans' favor.

Karen crawled along the American lines taking photos of the American troops fighting. Some were wounded and being treated by corpsmen. Some had been killed and were covered with plastic ponchos that billowed revealing the corpses underneath when helicopters flew over or the wind kicked up. She was terrified when the Viet Cong launched a human-wave attack trying to overrun the American positions. The US soldiers fought them back using their weapons and calling in artillery strikes.

Once the assault had been subdued and the VC had retreated back to their reinforced positions, Karen couldn't help but think that yesterday she was eating eggs benedict for breakfast on the Hotel Continental patio while reading her mail. She was safe and comfortable. She felt something wet on her pants and looked down. Blood from a nearby wounded soldier had formed a small stream that trickled underneath her soaking her ass. She felt nauseated by the sight and ashamed when she realized that the soldier had died.

De Saussure secured a plane and flew overhead, directing his battalion commanders as they regrouped their men and evacuated casualties. He ordered more water, ammunition, and rations be flown in by helicopter. The heat and humidity were exhausting requiring his soldiers to rest more under trees to cool down. A soldier could die of dehydration during the hot season, their brains literally boiled.

During the evening, De Saussure ordered the four remaining attack companies to the east to form a perimeter to block enemy units moving toward the companies that had been attack during the day. It was a big jumble of companies, and De Saussure needed them organized before sunrise when he was sure the Viet Cong would attack again. Major Guy Meloy was in charge of the forces to the west, while Lieutenant Colonel Hugh Lynch commanded the forces to the east.

The next morning the communist forces attacked de Saussure's base at Tay Ninh with a heavy mortar barrage while additional enemy forces assaulted Suoi Cao to the south. De Saussure and his staff were unsure of the communist commander, Colonel Cam's true objective since none of the attacks seemed like his main effort.

Colonel Cam consolidated his forces in the heavy woods near Ba Hao northeast of Dau Tieng. Cam ordered the 3rd Battalion of the 101st Regiment to cross the river and occupy prepared position within the forest. Some of the bunkers were made of concrete while all had thick overhead log coverings and were positioned to mutually support one another. All the communist soldiers and positions were carefully camouflaged making them all but invisible to the Americans. The communists had interconnecting tunnels that allowed for rapid reinforcement. His orders to the Battalion commander: the Americans were to be allowed to enter the forest before he opened fire. Cam's hope was to tangle with the American lines beneath the forest canopy to prevent American artillery and air support from playing a role in the battle.

After the morning fog lifted, the American forces continued their sweeps to locate the communists they knew were out there waiting for them. When Melody led one of his three companies into the forest, all seemed calm and quiet… too quiet. The Viet Cong and NVA waited patiently as the Americans walked into a series of concealed fire lanes extending from the enemy bunkers. The communists were well protected with an extended line and reinforced positions. One moment it was quiet, and the next all hell broke loose with enemy machine-gun crews raking the American lines. Enemy mortar rounds added to the confusion launching hot shrapnel into the Americans diving for cover wherever they could find it.

The Americans had fallen into the communist ambush and were fighting for their lives as they took heavy casualties. Melody ordered a flanking move by one of his platoons, but it failed to find the end of the communist lines and was pinned down.

Karen and Bryant were inside the American force being assaulted by the communists. They lay flat on the ground, but there was little cover. Karen could see that Bryant, a veteran war correspondent, was anxious and looking for a way out. "These guys are in real trouble. We need to pull back," said Bryant.

"You go. You don't need to be here to do your job. I do. I'm gonna stay," said Karen.

"Okay, but I think you're crazy."

"You're not the first person that has told me that."

"You keep that pretty little head down, Karen."

"I will."

"Good luck," said Bryant crawling away from the gunfire and chaos.

Karen knew that the only way she could leave and still keep her pride was to take an incredible photo of something. She didn't know what it would be, but she knew she wasn't going to find it lying on the ground. She crawled along the American line taking photos of the pinned down soldiers fighting for their lives. As she approached the end of the American line, she still didn't have the photo she needed. She was unsure, then thought of Capa's words, "If your photos aren't good enough, then you're not close enough."

She could hear an enemy machine gun firing from front of the line. The American soldiers were hunkered down, only rising up to take a few shots at the enemy, then back to the ground where it was safe. She looked to the side and saw a narrow dip in the ground from a small, dried-up creek paralleling the enemy's position. She crawled into the dip and made her way down the dried creek bed. She was fairly sure she would run into an enemy position and be captured, killed, or wounded. She wasn't. Instead, the creek bed finally played out and disappeared. The machine-gun fire was more distant and there was no other enemy fire that she could hear. She crawled out of what was left of the dip and toward where she thought the enemy line might be. After searching for a good ten minutes, she found nothing. She had passed the end of the enemy line of bunkers. She was safe for the moment. She could make her way to the rear and escape, or she could move back toward the battle. She chose the latter and crawled back toward the enemy machine-gun position. She stayed in the long grass as much as possible, but when she got close, she realized the top of the grass moved whenever she crawled. The grass was a dead giveaway of her position and offered no protection. "Don't be a whimp, Dickson," she said to herself.

She crawled out of the grass and was able to see an enemy bunker up ahead and the end of a machine gun barrel firing, smoke rising from the hot metal. She knew from watching the American machine-gun teams that at some point, the VC team would need to change the hot barrel for a fresh one. Both gunner and loader would be occupied. That would be her chance to move closer. Closer? What a dumb idea!

After another four minutes, the machine-gun fire stopped. She watched as the end of the barrel disappeared inside the bunker. They were changing the barrel. She took a deep breath and crawled forward. There was a fallen log just few yards from the gun portal of the bunker. She crawled behind it and shimmied up to the end closest to the bunker. She pulled out her camera, focused, and waited. She thought that if she didn't make any sudden moves, the gunner wouldn't notice her even though the side of his face would be in her shot. A moment more and he reappeared. She dared not take a photo for fear he would hear the shutter. She was that close... just like Capa said. She waited until the machine gun again opened fire. She took a photo, then carefully cranked the film advance lever, and took another. She knew she had two great shots and didn't want to press her luck. She slowly shimmied back behind the log and crawled back to the dried creek bed.

When she arrived back at the end of the American line, it occurred to her that the soldiers might think she was the enemy sneaking up on their position and open fire on her. At that range, they wouldn't miss. "Bob Dylan! The Flintstones! Dick Van Dyke! McCale's Navy! Rachel Welch!" she yelled.

"Okay, okay. Shut up and get your ass behind us!" said an American soldier.

She crawled forward as quick as she could, keeping her head down. When she reached the Americans, she crawled behind them and tried to catch her breath. She couldn't believe what she had just done. It was insanely stupid, but she got away with it. "Where did you go?" said the soldier.

"I went to find the end of the enemy's line," said Karen.

"And did you find it?"

"Yeah. I think I did."

"Well? Where the hell is it?"

Karen had to think for a moment. She was a photojournalist and supposedly neutral. But she was also an American and didn't want to see any more American soldiers die if she could help prevent it. "There's shallow creek bed twenty yards in that direction," she said pointing. "Good cover if you stay low. After one hundred yards it runs out. Hang a right and start crawling toward the machine-gun fire. You'll find it."

"Thanks," said the soldier turning to his partner. "I'm gonna tell the sergeant. You stay here and keep them busy."

Turning back to Karen, he said, "Are you coming?"

"Yeah. I'm right behind you," said Karen.

They disappeared into the long grass.

Hearing that a crazy photojournalist had stumbled upon the end of the enemy lines, Melody ordered the two companies being held in reserve forward. With two more companies, Melody was able to extend his lines and threaten to flank the communist positions.

Artillery rained down with much of it exploding in the trees and sending flying shards of wood into the communists and the Americans. Within an hour, all the American companies were pinned down and taking casualties. Melody radioed for more reinforcements. Two more American companies came to the rescue and were immediately pinned down by ferocious communist machine-gun fire from blocking positions.

A third company from the east commanded by Captain Robert Garrett engaged a communist platoon attempting to flank Melody's lines. It was a quick victory for the Americans. The communist platoon took heavy casualties before disengaging and retreating away from the battlefield. For some unknown reason, de Saussure ordered Garrett to reverse direction and link up with Lynch's force which would arrive the next morning.

Four hours into the firefight and after three communist human-wave assaults that nearly overran Melody and his soldiers, another American company from the 2/27th landed by helicopter just west of Melody's position. As they set out toward the battlefield, the Americans were engaged by an NVA blocking position and came under heavy machine-gun fire. It seemed the communists had figured out the exact route the Americans would take to reinforce their besieged forces and had built reinforced defensive positions to ambush the rescue effort. However, Melody persisted on attempting to rescue the besieged company. In two separate attempts, Melody sent a company through gaps in the communist line, only to find a line of enemy bunkers that drove his men back. His second attempt created a huge firefight and also failed to break through. Thirteen Americans died in the two attempt to rescue the company during the night.

Artillery strikes were ineffective on the enemy bunkers and could not be used to force a wedge between the communists and American lines for fear the artillery would hit their own men. At times, the fighting became hand-to-hand. As the sun rose on another day of fighting, both sides were exhausted.

De Saussure's superiors were watching the battle closely and didn't like what they were seeing. Several generals flew out to the brigade command post at Dau Tieng. De Saussure showed them his plan to rescue his forces. His superiors found the plan confusing and complicated. They sensed a disaster in the making. When they flew back to Bien Hoa Air Base, they asked Weyand to replace De Saussure with General DePuy and his 1st Division who were far more experienced at fighting the large force units that De Saussure's force had run up against. Weyand agreed.

As De Saussure and his brigade continued to fight it out with the communists, DePuy and his 3rd Brigade, 1st Division landed at Dau Tieng and moved to a staging position near the battlefield in preparation to attack the communists. The brigade needed to wait for their artillery to catch up. DePuy ordered de Saussure to break contact with the communists and pull back to a clearing where he could unscramble the eight companies under his command and return those companies to their original parent organizations. But before they could pull back, the brigade needed to rescue the lost company. De Saussare put Melody in charge of the battle and the rescue.

The next morning, Garret's company attacked south under a barrage of artillery. He and his men found the lost company which was in the process of fighting off another communist human-wave assault. Reinforcing the company's position, the two companies fought back the assault. Garret wasted no time as he was sure the enemy would attack again as the American forces began to break contact. The communists would make an all-out effort to destroy the lost company. With Garret's company acting as a shield for the survivors and wounded, both companies pulled back from the defensive position and moved to the west giving the enemy bunkers a wide berth. Four hours later, they were safe, and the wounded were evacuated.

With the lost company rescued, Melody ordered the remaining six companies to break contact and withdraw one-by-one under cover of artillery. As the companies withdrew, the American artillery was able to drive a wall of exploding shells between the retreating forces and the communists trying to pursue them. The communists took heavy casualties and finally allowed the American companies to break contact. Once they reached a landing zone, the American companies were extracted by helicopter and ferried back to Dau Tieng and Tay Ninh.

DePuy and his battalion took command of the operation. Over the next two days, two brigades of his brigades joined his forces at Dau Tieng and prepared to reengage the enemy. The Americans had found a large force of communists and they weren't about to let them go unscathed. DePuy was sure the communists would attempt to escape across the border in Cambodia. Instead of doing wide area sweeps, DePuy ordered his forces inserted into an area close to the suspected 9th Division headquarters and base.

De Saussure had used the technique of "jungle

bashing" where large units would sweep through the jungle trying to find the enemy. It deconcentrated his forces and made them ineffective when they finally found the enemy.

Since arriving in Vietnam, DePuy had concluded that the best way to engage the enemy was to send a small number of soldiers to find them, then once located, hit them with maximum manpower and firepower. To find the 9th Division, DePuy planned on using a technique call "cloverleafing" in which platoons would advance into an area and set up an overwatch position with machine guns and mortars. A squad would patrol forward 100 yards while another squad would patrol 100 yards to one of the platoon's flanks. If the squads found nothing, they would return to the platoon overwatch position which would move forward to another position and start the process over again. The cloverleaf technique allowed platoons to search an area thoroughly while reducing the risk of ambush.

Once his task force was assembled, DePuy flew one of his battalions by helicopters to the battlefield 196th had vacated. Two more battalions were flown seven miles further north where the communist headquarters were believed to be located. A Special Forces battalion of Nungs had tangled with the 101st Regiment in the area and had been badly mauled. Although two of DePuy's battalions immediately made contact with the enemy upon landing, they were unable to continue the engagement until the rest of their forces had landed which wasn't possible with artillery shell falling in the area. The Americans chose to consolidate rather than continue the fight.

At sunset, a squad from 3rd Brigade performing

ambush patrol spotted 150 Viet Cong slipping south toward Route 13. The American patrol called in artillery strikes as they set up claymore mines parallel to the trail the VC were using. When the artillery hit the VC column, the American patrol set off their claymores. Within minutes, seventy VC were killed without any American loses.

As the rest of the American battalions arrived, night set in and they formed up strong defensive positions which were attacked sporadically throughout the night, but no major engagement developed. The American artillery pounded suspected enemy positions throughout the night.

When morning came, the Americans found over 100 dead Viet Cong around their perimeter killed by artillery. DePuy's Brigade had one killed and twenty-three wounded.

Impressed by the results, Weyland ordered more battalions into the area under DePuy's command to find the enemy before it could escape.

Having bivouacked in a savanna grass clearing for the night, 1st Battalion, 28th Infantry Regiment, commanded by Lieutenant Colonel Jack Whitted received word that his men would be helelifted in the morning to another area. His men had set up two layers of Claymore mines around their perimeter. Early the next morning, the battalion's listening posts picked up movement in front of their position. Whitted ordered everyone back into the perimeter, then carried out reconnaissance by fire with mortars on the northern edge of his perimeter. The mortars set off two trip flares and the enemy troops hidden in the tall grass opened fire.

A few minutes later, the Viet Cong launched a

frontal attack against Whitted's position. As the Viet Cong human-wave approached, the Americans set off their outer row of Claymore mines. The Viet Cong were cut down in swaths as each mine took its toll. The VC recoiled and fell back. Whitted requested artillery strikes but the battery supporting his battalion was already moving to its new location. Instead, Whitted would use what he had onsite – mortars. Shells pounded the enemy positions as they formed up for another assault.

By the time the VC were ready to assault the Americans once again, the howitzers supporting Whitted's battalion were set up and ready to fire. Unaware of the additional danger, the VC launched their second assault storming toward the American perimeter. The howitzers cut them down but could only get so close to Whitted's perimeter. The surviving VC continued their advance until they came to the second line of Claymore mines that still had not been detonated. The Americans set the mines off launching thousands of steel balls into the VC soldiers. As before, they dropped in swaths, bodies falling in front of the Americans' position. Again, the VC pulled back but when they did, they were forced to run through the howitzers wall of exploding shells. More VC died as they were pelted with hot shrapnel. Those that survived were completely demoralized by the ferocity of the American weapons.

A few minutes later, air support arrived, and the fighter-bombers laid into the VC positions with bombs, rockets, and Napalm cannisters.

Despite its heavy losses, the VC commander of the 101st sent a second battalion into the battle to destroy the Americans. This was exactly what DePuy wanted.

Now knowing where a large number of VC were located, he would destroy them by alternating artillery strikes and aerial bombardment while Whitted's battalion continued to engage the enemy. The VC could not bring themselves to retreat when there was an American battalion that could be destroyed within their sights. They believed it was just a manner of determination and commitment from their men.

Captain Euripides Rubio, a company commander, saw a colored smoke grenades meant to identify the enemy's position had been ignited too close to his lines. As American jets were approaching, Rubio sprang from his perimeter, picked up the smoking grenade, and ran toward the enemy line. He was shot several times but kept advancing until he threw the grenade into the VC lines. The VC cut him down and he died having saved his men. He was later awarded the Medal of Honor posthumously.

The Americans too were taking heavy losses, some by sniper hidden trees behind their position. Whitted used his own snippers from his reconnaissance units to deal with the VC snipers. After several hours of a deadly game of cat and mouse, the VC snipers were finally cleared from the trees. But their damage had been done. Whitted's battalion was no longer combat-effective enough to withstand the enemy assaults. DePuy reluctantly ordered Whitted to withdraw his battalion. As the American's withdrew, the VC disengaged and made a run for the border and their Cambodian camps where they could regroup and resupply. Although the Americans tried, they were unable to stop the 101st from escaping.

After the VC had withdrawn, the Americans sent out patrols and discovered an enormous supply complex holding tons of grenades, mines, food, and clothing. They also discovered eighty-five VC bodies stuffed in a tunnel bringing the total VC loses to 390 killed. The Americans had lost nineteen killed during the action.

Operation Attleboro went on for almost another month which including several more battles between the communists and the Americans. While both sides claimed victory for having driven their opponent from the field, the real victory was for the Americans which had thrashed the communists with a one-to-seven body count. There were 155 Americans killed, 494 wounded, and five were missing. The communists suffered 1016 killed and over 200 missing or captured. The Americans also captured and destroyed sizable caches of food and supplies disrupting Viet Cong's supply chain. However, the Americans had failed to eradicate enemy political domination in Tay Ninh Province when the Viet Cong returned from their Cambodian bases.

THE YELLOW PARROT

Saigon, South Vietnam

When Karen and Bryant flew back to Bien Hoa Air Base on the outskirts of Saigon, they were beyond dirty and smelled similar to wet horses that had rolled in manure. Their clothes were stained with grass, mud, and puss from the elephant grass cuts that had become infected and burst. There was blood and lots of sweat. Mixed together, it formed a pungent aroma. Even the wounded soldiers flying back sat away from them. Karen agreed with them. All she wanted was a hot shower and ten to twelve hours of sleep. Food would be a priority when she woke, but for the moment, it was low on the list. Burning her clothes was high on the list, but she wasn't sure where she could do that. It too might have to wait.

When they landed, Karen surprised herself and took a taxi to the AP office where the film processing lab was located. Sleep and a shower would have to wait. She needed to see her photos. Bryant went with her. Her photos would be part of the article he would write and would help determine how well it sold to the newspapers and magazines subscribing to AP. Bryant had gone through a lot to get his story straight. He wanted a lot of people to read about what had happened.

Arriving at AP headquarters in Saigon, Karen and Bryant entered the office. Their co-journalist caught a whiff of them walking past and groaned in pain. "That's success you smell in case you were wondering," said Bryant loudly.

Karen laughed as she entered the lab area and handed off her film canisters to the technician. She gave him very specific instructions on how she wanted them processed. She had gotten over her shyness about insulting the experienced technicians. Even a veteran technician could make a mistake when it came to film processing, and she wasn't having any of it.

She sat in a chair outside the lab and closed her eyes for a moment, until someone shook her awake and said, "They're ready."

It was Bryant sitting next to her like a watchdog. Taking a moment to get her bearings, she looked up at the technician and said, "How'd they turn out?"

"See for yourself," said the technician motioning her into the dark room.

She and Bryant walked in and saw the prints hanging from the drying wire. "Wow," said Bryant with a big grin. "Those are really something."

"Yeah," said Karen. "Thank, God, they're in focus."

Bryant and the technician laughed.

Karen checked in to the Hotel Continental where the

desk clerk asked if she wanted to have someone pick up her clothes for laundering. "You don't think they're hopeless," said Karen.

"Possibly, but I am sure they will do their best to get them clean," said the clerk.

"Okay. Give a shot if you're willing."

Karen grabbed her room key and headed through the lobby toward the elevator. Patrons caught a hint of her odor as she passed, and she wondered if she had just single-handedly destroyed the Hotel Continental's reputation as a quality establishment.

Entering her room, she closed the door and peeled off her clothes. She put them in a laundry bag along with the clothes in her rucksack which were also beyond soiled. Stripped naked, she had nothing to change into after her shower, but she didn't care about that at the moment. That was tomorrow's problem when she woke up. She grabbed an apple from the complimentary fruit basket and headed into the bathroom.

She turned on the shower and devoured the apple while she waited for the water to get hot. Steam rose to fog the glass shower walls and the giant mirror above the sink. She pitched the core of the apple into a wastepaper basket and stepped into the shower. The water felt better than any sex she had ever had and immediately relaxed her. Her eyes closed and she almost fell asleep standing up. It took every ounce of energy she had left to scrub herself clean with soap and wash her hair twice because once was not enough.

When she walked out of the bathroom wearing a complimentary robe, she saw that the bag of laundry was already gone. "You, fools," she said to herself as walked over to the bed and climbed beneath the covers.

Twelve hours later, there was a knock at the door. She climbed out of bed and opened the door. Her laundry was done. She tipped the delivery woman and opened the bundle. She was amazed. Her clothes were actually clean. "Now, that's what I call service," she said to herself.

She picked up the phone, asked for room service, and ordered eggs benedict, a pitcher of orange juice, and a bottle of champagne. She had gotten close to take great photos and survived the unsurvivable. She felt normal again. She was going to make the most of it.

Nursing a Yellow Parrot cocktail, Karen sat on a couch in the hotel's rooftop lounge. She figured she was owed a couple of days' rest after her ordeal during Operation Attleboro. Her body would tell her when it was time to return to work. Not yet. She had dozens of little cuts on her face and arms. Not an attractive look, but she didn't care. She had earned her battle scars and wore them proudly. She was alone and not looking for company, hence the table. If a woman wanted company, she sat at the bar. Hookers sat at the bar and could be confused with regular women. Both were on the hunt for a man, but for different reasons. Karen wasn't interested in either.

She was watching two civilian men sitting at a table across the lounge. One of the men was facing her. She didn't recognize him, but she knew the type. He was CIA. She was sure of it. The other man she couldn't see as his back was facing her. But there was something about his hair that she found attractive. It was cut short but not Marine-short and it was neatly combed which said to her that the man paid attention to detail. He had used Pomade to hold it down from the evening breeze, but not so much that it looked greasy. She wanted to walk over and touch it but realized the idea was coming from the second Yellow Parrot she was drinking.

She watched as the CIA guy rose, paid the bill, and walked away. She glanced at him as he passed her table. Yep. He had that look – like he could smile while killing you and think nothing of it. His type was to be avoided and she felt better when he left the lounge.

The nice hair guy took a minute to finish his beer as he looked out at the city. He turned his head for just a moment, and she recognized him. It was Granier. She felt embarrassed but realized she had no reason to feel that way. She hadn't done anything. She felt like a high school freshman with a crush on a senior. Weird. Granier rose and walked toward the exit. Karen turned away looking in the opposite direction. Her face was flush. This is stupid, she thought. She looked at a shadow next to her own and turned to see Granier standing in front of her table. "Did you get in a fight with your cat?" he said.

"What?" she said, then it occurred to her that he was referring to her little cuts. "Oh, those. Elephant grass."

"Mmm… I'd rather piss off a cat."

"Yeah, well… I wasn't given a choice. I don't have a cat… or a dog for that matter."

"No pets?"

"I had a horse growing up. Actually, he was my mother's, but she let me ride him. Damned thing liked to step on my feet to let me know he was the real boss."

"That had to hurt."

"Oh, yeah. I could hear the bones in my toes crack."

"What in the hell are you drinking?"

"It's called a "Yellow Parrot. Equal parts absinthe, apricot liqueur, and yellow Chartreuse, whatever that is."

"Sounds deadly."

"Maybe. I'm only on my second. Do you want a drink?"

"You're asking me if I want a drink?"

"Yeah. It's called Women's Lib. It's becoming a thing back in the states."

"Where women ask men out?"

"Among other things."

"Okay. I'll have a beer."

"Nope. I said a drink. Beer and wine are for pussies."

"Are you calling me a pussy?"

"Only if you order a beer."

Granier thought for a moment. He wasn't sure if he liked her. But he wanted to find out and sat down across from her, then said, "I'll have a Yellow Bird."

"A Yellow Parrot. And no. That's far too foo-foo for a man like you."

"Okay, mistress. What can I have?"

"A martini I think."

"Can I at least have an onion instead of an olive?"

"That would make it a Gibson and yes you may."

Karen called over a waiter and ordered Granier's Gibson and another Yellow Parrot for her. "Are you sure that's safe?" said Granier.

"Why? Are you gonna take advantage of me?"

"Probably not."

"That's a shame. Anyway, I spent this last week getting my ass shot at by a bunch of communists. I'm pretty sure I can handle another Yellow Parrot."

"That's where I've seen you before. You're a photojournalist."

"Bingo. And you're a sniper… or a spy… or both."

Granier looked around to ensure nobody was close enough to hear her. He was okay for the moment, but he was liking the situation less and less. The waiter served the cocktails. "Do you mind if I touch your hair?" she said.

"Knock yourself out," he said and leaned over.

She pushed her fingers into his hair and shook them. "That's what I thought?"

"What's that?"

"Not too greasy. You wanna touch my hair?"

"Maybe later."

"I'm blowing it, aren't I?"

"I think you're a little drunk."

"I think you're right. The third Yellow Parrot is a killer… like you."

"Lady, you don't know anything about me," said Granier as he rose.

"Sit down. Please. I'm sorry. I'll shut up."

"If you shut up, I won't learn anything about you," said Granier sitting back down.

"Is that something you want… to learn about me?"

"I thought I did. I guess I still do. You are spirited I'll give you that."

"Do you like spirited?"

"You could say that."

"Are all your women spirited?"

"Only the ones that matter."

She smiled. "You remind me of a woman I knew," said Granier.

"A lover?"

"More than that. A kindred spirit."

"What happened to her?"

"She tried to kill me."

"Wow. I bet that put the kibosh on things."

"You could say that."

"Did you… kill her?"

"No. I could never do that."

"So, you're still in love with her."

"No. It's over."

"I think I'm going to throw up."

"Here? I think they frown on that."

"I'm not sure it's an option."

"I'll help you to the ladies' room."

"No. I hate throwing up in public restrooms. I never know what's been on the floor. I have a room here."

"Can you hold it that long?"

"I think so. It's worth the risk."

"Okay. Let's go," said Granier signaling the waiter for the check and pulling out a twenty.

Granier opened the door just in time. Karen dashed for the bathroom and slammed the door shut. Granier could hear her retching. It was not a pleasant sound but nothing Granier had not heard before. After a few moments of standing, unsure if he should leave or stay, he sat down in a chair figuring that he would wait a while and make sure she was okay. It was unusual for Granier to care about anyone, especially a person he just met. But she still intrigued him. She wasn't like other women.

After a few minutes, the retching sounds from the bathroom diminished. Karen emerged looking like death warmed over. Instead of crawling into bed, she walked over to Granier and curled up in his lap.

"Sorry," she said.

Granier didn't know what to do, but he didn't dislike it. He said, "It's okay. Go to sleep."

She did. Granier wrapped his big arms around her to keep her from rolling out of his lap. He stayed all night.

In the morning, he awoke. Karen was still asleep in his lap. He lifted her up and put her in bed. He wrapped her in the bedspread, then went into the bathroom and retrieved a drinking glass which he filled with water and placed it on the nightstand next to her. When there was nothing more to do, he left quietly hoping that his kindness toward her did not soften his aggressive attitude. He was a warrior and wanted to stay that way. No woman was going to change that... no matter what. Besides, he was old enough to be her father.

THAYER AND IRVING

September 23, 1966 – Binh Dinh Province

On the central coast of South Vietnam, Binh Dinh Province had a population of 875,000 in vast rural areas filled with farms and villages. It had long been a communist stronghold and had most of the population supporting the Viet Cong and NVA troops hidden in the densely forested mountains and narrow river valleys.

The ARVN forces in the province focused their efforts on controlling the larger towns, Highway 1 along the coast, and Highway 19 which led from the coast to the city of Pleiku in the highlands. The rest was VC territory.

Since the US 1st Calvary Division had arrived, it had tangled with the Viet Cong several times racking a large number of enemies killed and captured. They had driven the VC out of the villages and small towns only to watch them come back as soon as the incursion ended, and the Americans left.

The status quo changed when a VC platoon launched a mortar attack on Camp Radcliff, 1st Cavalry's base. 119 mortar rounds hit the base in a period of five minutes, killing four soldiers and wounding seventy-six. In addition, the VC mortars damaged seventy-seven out of 400 1st Cavalry's helicopters. While the damage was far from debilitating for the robust cavalry troops, it really pissed them off.

A week later, the VC and NVA attacked several ARVN military bases and ambushed an ARVN convoy bringing supplies and ammunition from the coastal ports. The brazen attacks showed how fragile the ARVN's hold was on the area. If left unchecked the VC and NVA could drive the ARVN out of the area giving the communists full control over the people, something they really wanted.

The Americans devised Operation Thayer, and later Operation Irving, to clear out the communists in the province and destroy the long-established Viet Cong infrastructure once and for all. They would pacify Binh Dinh Province whether the people wanted it or not.

The largest air assault operation up until that time in Vietnam, Operation Thayer focused on the Kim Son Valley. In an area the Americans called the Crow's foot, seven small rivers separated by steep mountains merged into one river. 1st Cavalry had tangled with the communists before in the same location during Operation Masher. After the Americans had left, the communists had simply moved back into their bases.

The operation started with several days of B-52 airstrikes where the Americans believed the communists were hiding. Next, General John Norton airlifted five airmobile battalions into the highlands above the valley floor. The Americans quickly descended into the valley from five different directions hoping to catch the communists off guard. The Americans found few enemy units to fight. The communists had fled from the valley at first sight of the helicopters. Even with 231 VC/NVA killed against thirty-five dead Americans, Operation Thayer was a disappointment when considering the massive number of American troops and resources used.

The failed mission was followed up with Operation Irving which slid the operation area east to the small mountain ranges near the coast. Intelligence reports revealed that the NVA 12th Regiment had fled there during the raid on the Kim Son Valley. Norton had five American battalions, five South Korean battalions, and two South Vietnamese battalions with a total of around 6,000 soldiers. Each of the national battalions would search a different mountain massif. When the enemy was found, the battalions would concentrate and squash the communists before they could escape.

The biggest problem facing the operations was the densely populated area in and around the mountains and coast. Leaflets dropped from aircraft instructed the civilians, mostly farmers, to stay in their villages when the fighting broke out. If their village came under attack, they were to flee only in the direction of the allied soldiers and not the communists.

Once again, the twelve allied battalions were airlifted into position. American reconnaissance units observed VC/NVA units in and around the village of Hoa Hoi. An American platoon was sent to investigate by helicopter and took heavy fire as it approached the village and suffered casualties. More American units were swiftly flown to the area and the village was surrounded. The Americans offered the inhabitants to leave the village unharmed. Two hundred civilians took them up on their offer and fled the village as the sunset.

As darkness fell, US Navy ships offshore fired

illumination rounds over the village all night to prevent the communists from escaping through the American siege ring.

The next morning the Americans began their assault with two companies advancing on the village from the north. The communists were forced to stand and fight or attempt to break through the well-reinforced American lines that surrounded the village. The Americans attacked with ferocity as they rooted out the communists destroying the village in the process. Before the next sunset, the battle was over. The Americans had won claiming 233 VC/NVA dead and thirty-five prisoners. The Americans had lost six soldiers.

1st Cavalry and the other allied forces continued to hunt down the communists in the area. 1st Cavalry shifted their search westward to mountains around the Kim Son and Suoi Ca Valleys.

The South Korean and South Vietnamese forces also fought with the VC/NVA. The Americans provided helicopter gunships that were helpful in the steep mountain terrain. Even though 135 VC/NVA soldiers were killed during the running gun battles, the allied forces were unable to locate and engage large enemy elements.

The allies were able to cobble together 681 VC/NVA killed and 1,409 captured while only losing fifty of their own soldiers killed during the entire operation. Operation Irving was declared a great victory by the Americans.

Like the previous operations in the area, Operation Thayer II focused on the Kim Son Valley and southwards to the Suoi Ca Valley. The Americans believed that the VC/NVA had broken into smaller units to avoid the sweeps from Operation Irving. But Thayer II ran into problems with the heavy monsoon rains while traversing the steep mountainsides in search of the enemy. Many ankles were sprained and broken after slips on the slick mud and foliage.

As the allied forces pushed on with their search, civilian casualties were rising rapidly. The commanders decided to empty the valleys of all inhabitants and declare the area a free fire zone. Anyone found by the allied patrols could be shot without retribution from their commanders.

Airstrikes and artillery bombardments were unrestricted. Non-combatants that stayed in the valleys to protect their homes and farms were to be considered enemy collaborators and were treated the same as the Viet Cong. They would be added to the final body count.

East of the Kim Son Valley, the Americans fought a large VC/NVA unit. Taking advantage of the steep terrain, the enemy anti-aircraft guns shot down three American helicopters that crashed in the mountains killing many of the airmen and their passengers. Thirty-four Americans were killed during the battle against ninety-five communists dead.

To prepare for a planned move into Binh Dinh, General Norton consolidated his forces. Assigned to the Suoi Ca and Vinh Thanh valleys, Colonel James Shanahan was the commander of the 3rd Brigade, 25th Division. Norton kept his 1st Brigade in the Kim Son Valley and assigned his 2nd Brigade to the Cay Giep and Mieu Mountains to the north. To improve his control over his forces, Norton established a forward division command post thirty miles northwest of Qui Nhon.

One of the patrols sent out by Shanahan discovered a series of caves among huge granite boulders in the Suoi Ca Valley. The triple-canopied vegetation concealed the cave entrances from allied reconnaissance flights. While investigating one of the caves, the Americans heard the voices of children and women. They ordered them out of the cave, but there was no response. Not wanting to harm women and children, the company commander and one of his sergeants entered the mouth of the cave and crept down a tunnel. After a few moments, they entered a large cavern occupied by Viet Cong. The American commander was shot dead. The sergeant fired back as he grabbed the commander's body and dragged it through the tunnel and out the mouth of the cave.

Outside, the Americans tossed tear gas canisters and smoke grenades into the tunnel to flush out the occupants. It didn't work. The Viet Cong fired their weapons and tossed grenades through the smoke and out the entrance. Unable to get the Viet Cong to surrender, the Americans used flame throwers to deplete the oxygen and suffocate anyone inside the tunnel. The resistance slowed and finally stopped. It was calm.

The Americans waited a few minutes for the oxygen level to rise before cautiously entering the tunnel. Entering the cavern, they discovered no bodies of women or children but several dead Viet Cong men. Moving further into the cavern they realized that the cavern was connected to a series of tunnels. Some tunnels led to exits, while others led to supply areas holding equipment, ammunition, and food. They also found a large number of records, including weapons and equipment lists, personnel rosters, a complete local order of battle, ammunition status reports, and, most importantly, a map showing the locations of caches throughout the province. The Americans had uncovered the Viet Cong's political headquarters for Binh Dinh Province. The Americans also uncovered several classified ARVN documents containing information about allied installations and a list of all allied radio frequencies and call signs. Everyone suspected that the ARVN had moles. The documents the Americans found proved it.

After the entire tunnel complex was thoroughly searched, US engineers detonated charges in one cave that set off a series of secondary explosions and blew a 100-yard-long gap in the side of the hill. In all, eight major complexes were destroyed, and their entrances were sealed by explosive charges. It was a huge find for the allies and a major help in tracking down the Viet Cong and NVA units in the province.

The monsoons hindered combat and logistic operations. Supply roads and highways were washed out by the heavy rains. Even the steel-mesh runway used by cargo planes was compromised by the rains and reduced supply runs to a trickle as deep ruts developed beneath the steel surface appeared. CH-47 Chinooks usually used to transport troops were forced to take up the slack and deliver food and supplies directly to the battalions in the field. 1st Cavalry used their own helicopters to fly in supplies which took some of the load off the squadron of Chinooks. The valleys turned into giant mud bowls making operations all but impossible.

When the rains finally let up for a few days, the Americans and their allies returned to their sweeps of the valleys and surrounding mountains. It was the ARVN forces that drew first blood with air and artillery support from the Americans. They engaged the 7th and the 8th Battalions of the 22nd Regiment killing over 250 VC/NVA.

A few days later, Norton received an intelligence report that suggested two Viet Cong battalions would attack Firebase Pony in the northern area of the Kim Son Valley in the next seven days. Norton wasn't taking any chances but didn't want to scare off the VC if it could be avoided. He airlifted 3rd Brigade headquarters along with one battalion from Camp Radcliff to Pony Firebase. As soon as the troops arrived and the headquarters set up, Norton received another intelligence report based on a Viet Cong deserter that said the 9th Battalion, 22nd Regiment was going to attack Air Base English at the end of the Tet truce. Norton deployed the 2nd Brigade to English and strengthened the base's defenses.

Yet another intelligence report from an intercepted radio call, identified the location of the NVA's 3rd Division command post in the An Lao Valley. Norton sent an entire battalion to find and destroy the command post. Although the Americans never found the headquarters, they did find another significant supply depot with tons of food and supplies.

Less than a week later, the ARVN 40th Regiment, 22nd Division, engaged an NVA battalion three miles from English. It was a fierce battle that ended up killing 100 NVA soldiers before the enemy battalion retreated back into the mountains. But the NVA were not done.

The next morning, they mortared English in a

savage barrage that killed or wounded fifty-two allied soldiers and damaged five helicopters. An uneasy, five-day truce for the Tet holiday began at 8 AM. It didn't last long. The enemy forces in the mountains fired on American aircraft flying around Air Base English. Intelligence reports continued to confirm that the VC/NVA would attack English once the Tet truce ended.

The communists didn't wait until the end of Tet and attacked an American unit in the Mieu Mountains between Landing Zone Hammond and Air Base English. Two battalions from the 2nd Brigade pursued the communist force but failed to engage them. The VC/NVA were once again leaving the valleys to the allies. Norton knew they would be back. It was only a question of when. He and his men had severely damaged the VC/NVA 2nd Regiment killing 1757 enemy soldiers while 242 Americans had been killed and 947 were wounded. Both sides had slugged it out in the mountains and valleys, and it was over, the communists that had come up wanting and left the battlefield.

Operations Thayer I & II and Operation Irving displaced a large number of villagers living in Binh Dinh Province. By the end of 1966, the province had eighty-five refugee camps holding 129,202 civilians. Even more civilians crowded into the towns and villages that had not seen fighting. Some became squatters along Highway 1 until it was safe to go back to their villages. But the allies had displaced the civilians in the Kim Son and An Lao valleys deliberately and did not want the villagers returning to the valleys which had been declared free fire zones where anyone was a fair target. The U.S. public relations officers declared the refugees as civilians fleeing communism. However, it soon became apparent that the South Vietnamese government's response to the refugee crisis was inadequate. Many people got sick and died from exposure to the monsoons. The refugee camps became hotbeds of discontent and effective recruiting grounds for the Viet Cong. Some refugee camps were considered unsafe for government officials and required military escorts when visiting and inspecting.

The Americans saw this as progress. The refugees were no longer able to support the Viet Cong living in the mountains around the valleys. With the refugees in guarded camps, it was difficult for the Viet Cong to recruit and extract even though the people were willing. However, many journalists argued in the press that the Refugee movement was a highly visible example of the South Vietnamese government's failure to protect the villagers and farmers from the Viet Cong.

October 14, 1966 – Washington DC, USA

After another fact-finding mission to Vietnam, US Secretary of Defense McNamara returned to Washington to prepare a report on the status of the war for President Johnson. Something had changed in McNamara. He had come to the realization that he had made a terrible mistake. He was depressed and found it hard to focus. How could he be so stupid and not see what was now plainly obvious to him – the Vietnam War was unwinnable?

It was Robert McNamara that had convinced the president, along with others, that he should commit ground troops to Vietnam. Now, they were dying by the hundreds, and at times by the thousands, every month. That was his doing. How could he possibly admit to such a blunder? And yet, how could he let it go on now that he realized the truth of it? He couldn't.

McNamara was a guy that believed in facts and analysis. When he went to Vietnam on this last tour and talked with the generals of MACV and embassy staff, he was confronted with data that he had a hard time believing. The communist forces were suffering losses of 60,000 killed per year and yet… "There was no sign of an impending break in enemy morale, and it appears that he can more than replace his losses by infiltration from North Vietnam and recruitment in South Vietnam. Enemy forces are larger; terrorist and sabotage have increased in scope and intensity; more railroads and highways cut; the rice crop expected to come to market is smaller; we control little, if any, more of the population in the countryside, the enemy almost completely controls the night."

The data showed that the North Vietnamese had increased their forces in proportion to the increase in American forces, which meant that the U.S. would be unable to achieve decisive attrition. More American troops would be met with more communist troops. Data also showed that the extensive air war America was waging against the north was ineffective at cutting off or even slowing the supplies and troops flowing into the south by means of the Ho Chi Minh Trail. The Americans were incapable of stopping the communist ant army that traveled and maintained the infamous supply route. As final evidence, the pacification programs in the southern countryside had failed and more villagers and farmers were supporting and even joining the Viet Cong.

As mighty as it was, America was losing the war. The U.S. policy that he had promoted had failed and would continue to fail. There was nobody to blame but himself. Like many American leaders and generals, he had underestimated the North Vietnamese. They were far more tenacious, determined, and resourceful than he ever imagined. And he had misjudged American military power against a rural society. And, he had overestimated the popular support of the South Vietnamese government and the effectiveness of the programs developed to strengthen the government's popular base. The conflict in Vietnam was caused primarily by political and economic effects which resisted a purely military solution.

McNamara was also deeply concerned with the antiwar movement that had erupted across the United States and was growing by the day, threatening to tear the country apart. He was troubled that many of the intellectuals and academics that he called friends and respected were opposing the war and questioning the White House's policies. Many of his closest friends such as Senator Robert Kennedy were quickly becoming some of the war's harshest and most public critics. It was all a big mess. A mess he had created. While others supported his programs, it was McNamara that was ultimately responsible. Even President Johnson was mostly following his advice and let him do most of the war planning. McNamara knew he had to do something, but what?

He would do what he had always done… write a report for the president explaining the data. But this time, his conclusions would be different, and he knew that the president would not be happy with what he had to say. He would say it anyway. He had to repair as much damage as he could no matter the president's ire.

Just like all of McNamara's reports, this one was filled with data in the form of easy-to-understand charts and graphs. When he briefed the president, he had the charts and graphs in the written report blown up for easy viewing. When that part of his presentation was done, McNamara started in on recommendations. Johnson was shocked by the direction McNamara was suggesting. McNamara no longer wanted to increase troop deployments as General Westmoreland had requested. He wanted a 500,000 cap placed on troops-in-country. Westmoreland was planning on 700,000 as per his request. McNamara was also encouraging another bombing halt and offering the Viet Cong a voice in governing the south. He wanted the north to enter into peace negotiations and needed bait for them to agree. He wanted to put even more pressure on the South Vietnamese government to increase the pacification programs and enact the political reforms that the people were demanding. McNamara now wanted a political settlement with the north, not a military one. He was putting as much on the table as he dared to hope the north would finally bargain with the U.S.

What McNamara was not suggesting was just as important as what he was suggesting. McNamara was not pressing for any kind of military withdrawal or an unconditional cease-fire both of which the North Vietnamese had demanded as conditions for opening peace talks. He also did not change his basic concept that the primary aim of the American military and foreign policy should be designed to contain communist expansion. Johnson was far from happy with the presentation and bombarded McNamara with questions about his shift in attitude about the war and its future direction.

As word spread about McNamara's mutiny against the administration's policy on Vietnam, he was ostracized by the other advisors, cabinet members, and the Joint Chiefs of Staff. Johnson himself started avoiding McNamara by canceling scheduled one-on-one meetings. The president wanted his supporters with him when speaking with McNamara.

It was during this time that McNamara started a study about American involvement in Southeast Asia that would one day result in the scandal called "The Pentagon Papers." McNamara knew that the writing was on the wall, and it was just a matter of time before Johnson asked for his resignation. He wanted to leave something behind that would help future presidents and generals make good decisions before starting a war. The study officially titled Report of the Office of the Secretary of Defense Vietnam Task Force would be his legacy. Slowly, McNamara was coming to terms with what he had done and moving to what he believed was the right side of history.

October 21, 1966 – Vientiane, Laos

When General Phoumi Nosavan was forced into exile in February 1965, he could no longer protect his supporters and subordinates. The commander of the Royal Lao Air Force, Brigadier General Thao Ma, was Nosavan's subordinate and one of his biggest supporters. The Laotian generals in the opposing faction wanted Ma out of the way. Generals Kouprasith Abhay, Oudone Sananikone, and Ouane

Rattkone plotted against Ma. On July 3, 1965, a land mine blew up under the vehicle holding Ma and his entourage. The assassination attempt failed, and Ma survived. Few argued over those responsible. While they had failed, the generals that opposed Ma were not hiding.

By the end of the year, tempers flared over the use of three C-47 transport planes that had recently been delivered from the United States. The generals demanded that the planes be transferred to one of the air bases near their headquarters so they could use them as they saw fit. Ma refused, saying they were needed to transport military supplies and troops, not the generals' personal opium and gold. To retaliate against Ma, promotions within the RLAF were severely limited angering the aviation officers and pilots.

Ma was criticized for using the military's aircraft to interdict shipments on the Ho Chi Minh Trail instead of flying close air support on the Army's ground campaigns. The generals ordered that Ma was to be removed from his command of the air force and replaced by Sourith Don Sasorith. The Laotian pilots mutinied. But the generals did not back down and threatened to throw the pilots in the brig if they did not obey their superiors.

Ma met in secret with his fellow conspirators Generals Bounleut Saycocie, Thao Ty, and Nouphet Daoheuang. For five nights, they planned their revolt against the General Staff.

On June 2, 1066, General Nouphet's regiment surrounded the Savannakhet Airfield. The insurrection failed when the two other generals lost their courage and took no action. It was over in forty-eight hours. As a compromise, the transport aircraft were broken off into a separate military airlift command under Sourith, while Ma took over fighter operations. Ma immediately moved his dozen T-28 aircraft and thirty pilots along with their maintenance crews to Luang Prabang in the north. Although Ma continued to feel threatened by the generals, King Sisavang Vatthana protected him from being removed from his command. But for Ma, a man with a fighting spirit, that wasn't enough. He wanted control over his own destiny.

On October 20, 1966, Generals Ouane and Bounthone Marthepharak were in Savannakhet, on a tour of military their forces. They had a loyal guard unit escort them as they traveled. Ma was unimpressed and believed it was time to strike. Ma had put together $31,000 US in a fund to bribe the officers of two nearby regiments. Nouphet would use his regiment to apprehend General Ouane and General Bounthone while on their tour of the airfield. Ma would lead an airstrike against the generals' headquarters in the capital of Vientiane. The second regiment would be airlifted to Vientiane where they would take over the city and arrest Kouprasith and Oudone if they survived the bombing.

But the night before the air assault, Ma confided in his assistant air attaché in Vientiane and told him to stay away from headquarters. At dawn, the coup began but not before the air attaché had warned headquarters of the pending bombardment. Generals Kouprasith and Oudone fled the headquarters just as the bombs began to drop.

Things went from bad to worse for the coup plotters as the money for the bribing of the regiment never showed up from Vang Pao. Angry from not being paid, Nouphet declined to arrest Ouane and

Bounthone. It was a disaster for the coup.

The one thing that went right was that Ma launched eight of his T-28s and assaulted the generals' headquarters, a gun park, two munitions depots, and Kouprasith's villa in Vientiane killing twenty-three of the generals' loyal supporters. With their ammunition and bomb racks empty, the T-28s headed for their air base to rearm.

As the planes landed, Ma had them prepped for a second attack on the capital. However, Prince Boun Oum, US Ambassador William Sullivan, and the British Ambassador flew to the airfield and convinced Ma not to attack for a second time. Instead, the coup air force technicians climbed aboard a transport plane and were escorted by Ma's T-28s and loyal pilots. They flew to Udorn Air Base in Thailand where they were all arrested by the Thai police after landing. The coup was over.

Ma and his supporters spent eight months in a Thai prison before being released and given political asylum from the Thai government.

In Laos, Ma was sentenced to death in absentia. He never went back to Laos. Ma's departure from the Royal Lao Air Force was a big blow to the military and morale within the RLAF fell to an all-time low. As planned, Sourith took command of the RLAF but was not well respected by those under his authority. Once assured of air transport, the generals began sending shipments of opium all over the world, including Vietnam where many American troops became their best customers of the injectable form of opium known as heroin. The generals grew rich off the Americans' addiction.

OPERATION SEA DRAGON

October 25, 1966 – Eastern Coastline, North Vietnam

There were three supply routes the North Vietnamese used to transport weapons, ammunition, and supplies to the Viet Cong and NVA forces in the south – The Ho Chi Minh Trail, the Red River Delta, and the Eastern Coastline.

The Ho Chi Minh Trail was by far the most famous and was able to enter South Vietnam from the western mountains where many of the Viet Cong and NVA bases were located. But the Ho Chi Minh Trail required a huge number of human resources to keep the convoys moving and was under constant threat from US bombers and MACV/SOG hatchet teams throughout Laos and Cambodia.

The Red River flowed from China into North Vietnam and became a dependable supply route. The river emptied into the Red River Delta in and around Haiphong Harbor. From there, weapons and supplies could be transported by land, sea, or river. The rivers in the Red River Delta were numerous and many continued down to South Vietnam. The problem, of course, was the border and the DMZ where South Vietnamese and American forces were stationed. Moving supplies across the border by land or river was a risky business for the North Vietnamese, especially when the Americans began bombing their routes.

The third supply route from north to south was the eastern coast by way of the Gulf of Tonkin. Far more supplies and weapons could be shipped by boat than dozens of trucks or hundreds of reinforced bicycles. But like the rivers flowing down into the south, the American Navy patrolled the coastline and caught many of the North Vietnamese supply boats disguised as fishing boats or sampans going to market. But even though many boats were caught, some got through and delivered their shipments to the Viet Cong waiting onshore.

Russian and Chinese ships were bringing supplies, ammunition, and weapons into Haiphong Harbor. They would not venture further down the coastline for fear of tangling with the US Navy. That meant that it was up to the North Vietnamese to figure out a way to get the supplies, ammunition, and weapons into South Vietnam. It wasn't easy and it was about to get a lot more difficult as the Americans began Operation Sea Dragon (originally named Operation Traffic Cop) in late October 1966.

The American destroyer, USS Mansfield, was once again ordered to go into harm's way as one of two destroyers forming the spearhead of the operation. Mansfield's companion was the USS Hanson. The two destroyers' main batteries were three twin five-inch/38 caliber Mark 38 dual purpose mounts. The five-inch guns were guided by a Mark 37 Gunfire Control System. The maximum range of five-inch cannons with a fifty-five-pound projectile was ten miles. The destroyers also had a large variety of weapons including Bofors anti-aircraft cannons, depth charges, and torpedoes. While a battleship's sixteen-inch cannons could reach twenty-four miles in range, the destroyers were far more maneuverable and ideally suited for coastal warfare among the hundreds of small islands.

At 5 AM on October 25th, Mansfield and Hanson took the lead and entered North Vietnamese waters beginning a new naval phase of the Vietnam War. Made up of American destroyers from the US Navy's 7th Fleet and a group of US cruisers and Royal Australian Navy vessels, the task force's orders were to "patrol the North Vietnam coastline from the demilitarized zone northward and destroy North Vietnamese waterborne logistics craft carrying arms and materials to enemy troops in the south."

The task force's main onshore targets were radar stations, boat repair facilities, surface-to-air missile sites, and bridges. In addition, the allied vessels would intercept and destroy enemy cargo vessels ranging from small sampans to large steel-hulled cargo ships and self-propelled barges.

The first engagement began in the Dong Hoi Gulf when the two American destroyers came upon several enemy logistic vessels. After a brief but fierce naval engagement, the enemy vessels were sunk. Onshore enemy artillery guns opened fire on both the Mansfield and Hanson which sailed to deeper waters out of range of the shore guns. From their new location, both destroyers opened fire with their main five-inch batteries at the enemy shore guns which were eventually silenced.

During the first week of Operation Sea Dragon, the two destroyers managed to sink 119 enemy vessels and damage another ninety-four. The American five-inch guns were superior to anything fired by the North Vietnamese vessels. No American sailors were wounded or killed and morale aboard the destroyers was high.

Unable to stop the American destroyers, the North Vietnamese were forced to move their supply depots further inland away from the coastline and use other methods of transport. Shipments to the south were severely curtailed during the US Naval operation. But the North Vietnamese were not defenseless. They camouflaged their coastal batteries and radar. Keeping the weapons' location hidden, the gunners waited until the American destroyers came within range before opening fire. Again and again, the enemy shore batteries were able to drive the American destroyer back out to sea while continuing to fire before they sailed out of range. And again and again, once they were safely out of range, the two US Destroyers would fire their main guns and destroy the onshore guns firing at them.

During the Sea Dragon Operation, the American battleship USS New Jersey sailed into the Bay of Tonkin. Coming out of a fifteen-year sabbatical since the end of the Korean War, the Iowa-class battleship had sixteen-inch guns and could reach eighty-five percent of the military targets in North Vietnam. On its first day of operations, the New Jersey destroyed a supply depot, a barracks, several key roads, 1,000 feet of occupied trench line, and an anti-aircraft battery that had tried to shoot down a Marine F-4 Phantom. After that, communist gun crews would abandon their coastal batteries as soon as they caught sight of the American battleship on the sea's horizon. Nobody wanted to tangle with the New Jersey. While she was not the most maneuverable vessel, she was the most powerful and ruled whichever sea she chose to sail. Even the enemy's fortified caves were no match for the ship's 2,700 lb. shells. Bridges and logistic complexes were completely destroyed with one hit from the New Jersey's guns.

Operation Sea Dragon continued for two years firing almost 14,000 shells with 2,000 enemy ships sunk or damaged. It was only President Johnson's 1968 halt to military missions that finally brought the naval operation to an end as the Navy's vessels were ordered back south of the demilitarized zone. In all those missions, only five American seamen were killed and twenty-six wounded from enemy shore battery fire. There was little question by either side that Operation Sea Dragon was an allied victory that had greatly hindered North Vietnamese logistical efforts to supply communist forces in the south.

October 25, 1966 – Cam Ranh Bay, South Vietnam

In Manila, President Johnson had attended a 7-nation summit on the war in Vietnam. After two days of talks, the attendees signed a joint resolution stating that American forces and its foreign allies would leave South Vietnam six months after North Vietnamese troops withdrew their forces from the south. By signing the resolution, Johnson and his allies thought were resolving the key issues in Hanoi's peace talk objections.

In a separate resolution, South Vietnam leaders also pledged to establish political, social, and economic reforms that would create a more stabilized country, including democratic elections within the year.

When the summit concluded, Johnson visited the island fortress of Corregidor where American forces had held out against the invading Japanese forces during World War II. Johnson suddenly turned to Lady Bird Johnson and said, "It's time to go."

He kissed his wife goodbye and boarded a waiting helicopter that flew him to an airfield outside of Manila. From Manila, Johnson secretly flew to Cam Ranh Bay Airfield in South Vietnam for a surprise visit. A small pool of eight reporters and four photojournalists accompanied Johnson in his plane. Informed of his visit only shortly before the president arrived, General Westmoreland, Ambassador Lodge, Secretary of State Dean Rusk, South Vietnam Premier Nguyen Cao Ky, and Chief of State Lieutenant General Nguyen Van Thieu greeted Johnson after he descended the stairs from the presidential plane. Everyone wanted a photo op. In the first visit to a war zone by an American president since President Roosevelt visited North Africa in 1943, 7,000 U.S. Troops lined up to see Johnson.

After presenting medals to five soldiers, Johnson surprised Westmoreland when he presented him with a Distinguished Service Medal. Johnson, unaccustomed to the heat and humidity, sweated through his shirt and several handkerchiefs supplied to him by one of his aides. Johnson spoke to the troops and said, "I could not come to this part of the world and not see you; the best-prepared army, the most skilled army, the most compassionate army, and the best-led army in the world. I give you this pledge… We shall never let you down nor your fighting comrades nor the fifteen million Vietnamese nor the hundreds of millions of Asians. One day the whole world will know what you have done here was worth the price."

With Westmoreland by his side in a jeep, Johnson inspected an honor guard representing the 325,000 American troops in Vietnam. After the inspection, the jeep continued to the 12th Air Force Field Hospital where Johnson and Westmoreland visited the wounded soldiers. The president presented twenty-four Purple Heart medals, and said to one wounded soldier, "You have the prayers of a grateful president and a grateful nation. We believe in you. And when peace comes, we will receive you in your homeland with great thanks and with great pride."

The president dined with the soldiers and proudly signed their hats on request. Johnson's entire visit only lasted two hours and twenty-four minutes before he returned to Manila, then onward the next day to Thailand to continue his far east tour.

October 26, 1966 – Gulf of Tonkin, USS Oriskany

Sailing in the Gulf of Tonkin on her second deployment to Vietnam, the USS Oriskany was an Essex-class aircraft carrier mostly supporting ground operations in South Vietnam.

As the vessel turned into the wind at 7:28 AM, the crew was preparing to start flight operations for the day and stowing ordinance from night operations. A Seaman was stowing several MK-24 magnesium flares unused during night operations in compartment A-107-M located just off the forward hangar deck, adjacent to the Starboard sponson. The Mark 24 magnesium flares were twenty-seven-pound metal canisters three feet long that would illuminate with the intensity of two million candlepower and burn for two and a half to three minutes while parachuting downward from an overhead aircraft.

When one of the flares was accidentally actuated, the panicked sailor threw the burning flare into the storage locker and slammed the door shut instead of throwing the ignited ordinance over the side into the sea. Hundreds of flares were stowed inside the locker and were ignited by the flare burning at 4000 degrees.

A fire alarm sounded, then general quarters throughout the ship. Firefighting teams raced to the location of the alarm location and found they were unable to open the door to the locker. The incredible pressure inside the locker pushed against the watertight door. Unable to open the door, the firefighting teams could not fight the fire directly. They began cooling down the walls around the compartment. It did little good as the heat inside the compartment created from the burning flares continued to rise like a pressure cooker.

Ten minutes after the fire started, the red-hot door blew out from the compartment and flew across the hangar deck where it hit and ignited a helicopter. Fight crews worked frantically to move aircraft loaded with bombs and fuel away from the engulfed flare compartment. Smoke and heat from the fire were drawn into the crew quarters forward from the hangar deck. The crew moved aircraft from the hangar deck to the flight deck as fast as the elevator would allow hoping to prevent explosions that would cripple the ship and put all their lives in peril.

More smoke filled the lower decks where much of the crew was located. The sailors used wet towels around their faces to prevent smoke inhalation and protect themselves from the heat. They tried to close the air vents pumping out smoke but were mostly unsuccessful. Sailors helped evacuate the officers' quarters where many of the pilots slept. The smoke was thick and blinding, stinging their eyes.

A huge explosion in the flare locker set off more of the flares and once again increased the heat and smoke pouring through the open doorway. Many of the firefighters were overwhelmed by the heat and smoke. As the temperature rose to unbearable heights, Aircraft on the hangar deck caught fire. Firefighters attempted to cool them down but were fighting a losing battle. The heat was too intense. A fireball shot down the passageway where the pilots were trying to evacuate their staterooms. Several were killed when their lungs were burned and suffocated.

On the flight deck, the steel deck was acting like a griddle, melting the flight crews' boots as they shifted bomb-ladened aircraft away from the intense heat. The flight crew pushed ordnance off the deck and into the sea to keep it from exploding.

On the hangar deck, the firefighters made saving the ship and its crew their highest priority. Any aircraft that caught fire, along with any ordnance, was immediately pushed over the side into the ocean. With little thought, millions of dollars in aircraft and ordnance were being destroyed by the minute. It was the only way to keep the fire from expanding further.

One of the pilots was trapped in his stateroom as

the fire raged in the passageway. He could feel his head getting dizzy from the lack of oxygen. He wrenched open the room's porthole and pushed his head out for fresh air. He attempted to climb out through the porthole, but his shoulders were too big. When the room began to catch fire, the pilot grabbed the sheets and blanket from his bed and soaked them with water. Wrapped in the wet sheets and blanket he once again stuck his head out the porthole. Steam rose from the sheets and blankets as the fire in the room intensified. The pilot was being steamed alive like a basket of shrimp. A seaman running past the porthole saw the pilot's situation. He grabbed an Oxygen Breathing Apparatus and handed it to the choking pilot through the porthole. The seaman also grabbed a firehose, fed it through the porthole, and turned on the water at the spigot. The grateful pilot slipped on the mask, then soaked everything in his room. He was still unable to leave through the passageway, but at least he had a fighting chance. Although severely burned by the fire and smoke, the pilot survived.

Many sailors and firefighters were trapped in the lower decks as they tried to evacuate personnel and keep the fire from spreading. Water from the fire hoses on the upper decks began to flood the lower decks and the watertight doors were shut cutting off the sailors' escape routes to the upper decks.

The inferno raged for two and a half hours before the firefighters and seamen were finally able to get it under control. The last fire was extinguished five hours later. The ship's crew was lucky to be alive. The Oriskany was heavily damaged and unable to stay at its station. Under its own power, the aircraft carrier set a course for Subic Bay Naval station in the Philippines.

Many of the injured seamen were flown to the USS Constellation.

Forty-four men had died in the fire and another 156 were seriously injured. The fire aboard the Oriskany was the first of three major aircraft carrier fires that occurred during the Vietnam War. A board of inquiry determined that the MK-24 flares could be ignited when jarred insistently and that was what had started the fire aboard the aircraft carrier. After one year and extensive repairs in San Francisco's naval yards, the USS Oriskany returned to Yankee station in the Gulf of Tonkin to resume its mission.

November 1, 1966 – Saigon, South Vietnam

It was National Day in South Vietnam commemorating the overthrow and assassination of the dictator, President Ngo Dinh Diem, and the rebirth of the country under the rule of a military junta. Spectators lined the streets of downtown Saigon watching as a military parade passed. Prime Minister Ky, a leader in the military junta, was standing on a platform saluting his troops.

The Viet Cong had been searching for a way to demonstrate the weakness of the Saigon government and the ARVN. By attacking civilians, they showed that the South Vietnamese military and their American allies were incapable of protecting the people. The parade was a perfect opportunity to score a public relations victory.

The night before the parade, the Viet Cong moved three recoilless rifles to the edge of a jungle three and a half miles away from downtown Saigon. It was a long shot for even the best recoilless rifle gunner. The gun crew set up the guns and hid them with additional camouflage.

As Ky inspected a new group of soldiers, a recoilless rifle shell rocketed overhead and exploded a dozen yards from the platform. It was close. Too close. The military commanders in the parade called for reinforcements as thirty shells exploded around the city. Civilians ran for cover or sped off on their motor scooters. American and South Vietnamese APCs blocked escape routes as they speed into the city center. Nobody knew if the Viet Cong and NVA would launch a ground assault once the shelling subsided.

One shell hit the Chapel of Saint Anthony of Padua in the Saigon Cathedral. Another exploded in front of the cathedral killing an American officer. Five more Americans were wounded, and two South Vietnamese civilians were killed when a shell landed in the crowded central market. Spotting the location of the recoilless rifles, military observers were amazed at the gunners' accuracy.

The terrorist attack was over shortly after it began. The Viet Cong disassembled their weapons and melted back into the jungle. When the allied armored vehicles arrived at the edge of the jungle the Viet Cong were long gone.

Hearing of the attack, former President Eisenhower said that the war had gone on too long and that America should be sending in the kind of military strength needed to win.

November 2, 1966 – Saigon, South Vietnam

Just as things were returning to normal the day after the parade attack, the Viet Cong struck again. A Viet

Cong soldier wearing civilian clothes smuggled a grenade into the Phu Tho Racetrack. During the third race, the soldier pulled the pin on the grenade and rolled it down the grandstand's wooden steps before mixing in with the crowd. The grenade exploded in mid bounce sending red-hot shrapnel into the crowd, killing an old man and his infant grandson. Eight more were wounded and rushed to a nearby hospital where surgeons dug out the pieces of shrapnel from the victims' scorched flesh.

The VC soldier responsible for the attack was never found. In urban warfare, there was no way to detect combatants from civilians. It was the reason the VC terrorists carrying out attacks rarely carried a weapon beyond the bomb or grenade they were going to use. If caught with a weapon, they were immediately arrested and usually executed shortly after an intense interrogation.

November 3, 1966 – Saigon, South Vietnam

The Viet Cong recoilless rifle teams returned on the third day of terrorist attacks in Saigon. This time they were bolder and set up their weapons on a rooftop on the outskirts of the city closer to their targets. When they opened fire, they hit the Ben Thanh Market, the Grall Hospital, the Saigon Cathedral, a Catholic seminary chapel, and several private homes in a wealthy neighborhood.

After firing twenty-four recoilless rifle shells, the Viet Cong once again disassembled their weapons and fled to the nearby jungle. The only evidence they left behind was the spend shell casings. Nobody was arrested for the attack that killed eight people and seriously wounded thirty-seven civilians, several of which were children.

The attacks at the beginning of November became known as the three days of terror. As the Viet Cong had hoped, the people of Saigon were angry and shouting for protection against the rebels. There was little the government could do beyond what they had already done which was basically nothing. Terrorist attacks in and around Saigon would continue throughout the war demoralizing the capital city's population.

November 30, 1966 – Saigon, South Vietnam

Through an emissary, the North Vietnamese and Viet Cong presented a proposal to South Vietnam and its allies – three ceasefires to coincide with the holidays. It was unusual for the North Vietnamese to offer any kind of proposal to the south and it was met with suspicion. It was the Americans at the embassy that saw the offer as a small, but genuine olive branch and convinced the South Vietnamese to accept the ceasefires.

The ceasefires would overlap three holidays. All fighting would halt for the Christmas holiday from 7 AM on December 24th to 7 AM on December 26th. Additionally, the New Year's holiday would have a ceasefire from the morning of New Year's Eve, 1966, until the morning of January 2nd, 1967. Lastly, the Tet holiday, celebrated by both North and South Vietnam as the traditional start of the Vietnamese new year, would see a halt in all fighting from February 8th through the 12th.

Both sides knew it was one thing to say there was

to be a ceasefire and it was another to actually have a halt in all fighting during that time. The war had dragged on far beyond what either side thought was reasonable and the combat troops on both sides were exhausted and needed a break. For the Vietnamese, it was an opportunity to visit with family and friends without fear of attack. And for the Americans, it was a time to eat traditional Christmas food, drink too much whiskey and beer, and catch up on their letter-writing to home. The constant fear of being attacked had a chilling effect on a soldier's mind. They welcomed the break even if it was for only a few days, but few thought it would last. Neither side trusted the other as far as they could throw them. And why should they? They were the enemy.

December 7, 1966 – Saigon, South Vietnam

As the Americans continued to cut off supplies and weapons being sent south with operations like Sea Dragon and Attleboro, the Viet Cong were determined to have their presence felt. They did everything in their power to disrupt the South Vietnamese government and show it as inept and corrupt. That's why Tran Van Van became their target.

Tran was a fifty-eight-year-old politician and the leading candidate for president of South Vietnam. Formerly the Secretary General of the nation's High National Council, Tran had been elected to the 117-member assembly to draw up the new constitution. It was a great and important honor. In a very real sense, the fate of the country was in his hands.

In early December, Tran went to symbolically "kiss the ring" of Prime Minister Ky, the most powerful leader in South Vietnam. When Tran left Ky's office, he climbed into his chauffeur-driven sedan and headed to his political headquarters. Pulling onto the main boulevard, a motorcycle with a man riding behind the driver pulled up next to the sedan. The Viet Cong assassin pulled out a revolver and fired at the backseat window. The window shattered after the first two shots. The remaining four bullets fired hit Tran and killed him. It was a tragic loss for the country which was just what the Viet Cong were hoping to accomplish.

December 19, 1966 – Vung Tau, South Vietnam

There was no shortage of rivers in Vietnam. Many started in the northern and western mountains and flowed into deltas by the sea in the north and south. In the regions with few roads which were often washed out by the monsoons, the Vietnamese depended on the rivers for transporting their crops to market. That made the sampan traffic down the rivers congested at times and a nightmare to patrol. The American and South Vietnamese patrol boats could not stop and search all the boats without greatly hindering commerce which was tough enough for civilians during wartime. The Viet Cong took advantage of the situation and used sampans to smuggle their weapons and supplies deep into the south. Some were caught, but most were not.

To deal with the predicament, the Americans developed a new fighting force that would come to be called "Mobile Riverine Force or MRF." The MRF was a joint US Army and US Navy force that formed a large part of the brown-water navy, the nickname for the allied boats patrolling the rivers and deltas. The MRF was developed based on the experiences of the French during the Indochina War. Their extensive river force was known as Dinassaut and used floating artillery to defeat the enemy on land and water. With more resources and the French experience as a guide, the Americans developed some very effective water-based weapon systems that only improved over time.

The Riverine force was originally designed to provide an all-weather "strike" capability that could actively engage the Viet Cong as they attempted to float their troops and supplies down the rivers and through the deltas. The Mekong Delta was especially problematic for the allied forces and an ideal venue to test riverine operations and weapons.

The MRF was made up of a variety of watercraft, especially at the beginning of the Vietnam War when World War II surplus naval craft were used. Many of the smaller landing craft, such as LCMs and LSVPs and the Norwegian-built Nasty class fast patrol boats, were ideal for the rivers and deltas while the larger craft, such as the LSMs, LSSLs, and PGMs had trouble maneuvering in the shallow and sometimes narrow rivers. The larger vessels were better suited for the wide rivers or as floating base camps where the smaller vessels could tie up and be protected during the night.

Some of the LCMs were converted to all-steel enclosed naval Monitors with a 40 mm gun, a 105 mm howitzer, or a flamethrower. Using long flaming streams of Napalm, the flamethrower version was especially effective against enemy rivercraft and jungle shore assaults. Each vessel also carried a variety of machine guns and onboard mortars. When their retrofit was completed, the newly rebuilt Monitors were sixty feet long, seventeen feet wide, with a draft of three and a half feet, and manned by eleven crewmen. The vessels were wrapped with ten tons of steel-plated armor and were powered by two Gray Marine diesel engines capable of eight and a half knots at full speed.

Riverine squadrons were paired with a reinforced brigade of Army infantry consisting of three infantry battalions and an artillery battalion, plus a headquarters company and other combat service units. The entire river assault force would be stationed on U.S. Naval ships anchored in the rivers. Each assault group was capable of transporting the combat elements of one entire infantry brigade into battle.

There was also a small salvage vessel to recover any damaged ships or craft. Several of the ships in each squadron were mounted with counter-mortar radar to guide the four and a half-inch mortars onboard the vessels. The vessels in each riverine squadron consisted of fifty-two Armored Troop Carriers (ATCs or "Tangos"), ten Monitors, thirty-two Assault Support Patrol Boats (ASPBs), five additional Monitors to serve as command-and-control boats, and two LCM-6s to serve as refuelers. The squadron was also accompanied by a salvage force of two 2,000-ton heavy lift vessels, two YTBs for salvage, two LCUs for utility craft, and three 100-ton floating dry docks. Several of the larger vessels also had helicopter landing pads on their decks for resupply by air and medical evacuation.

The first MRF force arrived at their floating headquarters at Dong Tam Base Camp west of My Tho in the Mekong Delta in early December 1966. Within ten days they would be in combat at Vung Tau along with the 2nd Brigade of the 9th Infantry Division.

Eventually, there would be four River Assault Squadrons formed – the 9th, 11th, 13th, and 15th. The 9th Infantry Division was assigned to all of the squadrons.

Before long, the Army developed floating artillery and mortar barges that could be positioned near the floating headquarters and support the planned area of operation of each assault. The mobile bases and assault squadrons were capable of operations in the furthest reaches of the Deltas. The US Army deployed the Riverine force similar to the way it would use an armored cavalry regiment but on water instead of land.

It was much easier for the Riverine vessels to keep their distance from the enemy, usually located on shore. The only real limitation was the width and depth of the river. The Zippo Monitors, as they were nicknamed after the popular cigarette lighter, could fire a 225-second stream of burning Napalm 200-300 yards in any direction from their rotating steel turrets. Ambushes and reinforced bunkers developed by the Viet Cong to attack the Riverine force were easily neutralized with the flamethrower. The sailors would make the Napalm by mixing a powder of coprecipitated aluminum salts of naphthenic and palmitic acids with gasoline. Compressed air from a storage tank propelled the Napalm through the barrel of the flamethrower while a gasoline lighter at the end of the barrel ignited the high-powered stream of sticky fluid.

When the infantry disembarked the landing craft, they were under the protection of the riverine force with their 40 mm guns and 105 mm howitzers mounted in turrets, 82 mm heavy mortars enclosed in a wall of steel plates, and Napalm flamethrowers. If they went beyond the range of the riverine's weapons, air support from a squadron of Navy gunship helicopters called the Seawolves based out of Dong Tam would take over and escort the Infantry until the completion of their mission.

The Riverine force was one of the most successful programs during the Vietnam War. Amazingly, some enemy weapons and supply smuggling operations continued throughout the conflict.

December 24, 1966 – Saigon, South Vietnam

Starting at 7 AM on Christmas Eve, a ceasefire came into effect for forty-eight hours in all of Vietnam. All attacks including aerial bombardment were to stop during the ceasefire. It didn't take long before it was violated. Australian troops were fired on by Viet Cong near Saigon. Six more violations of the ceasefire occurred including a small arms and mortar assault near Phu Loc in Thua Thien Province. One ARVN soldier was killed during the ceasefire.

The violations made many wonder how much control Hanoi had over its troops in the field, especially the Viet Cong. It was, of course, possible that the Viet Cong received orders to carry out the attacks from higher-up authorities. Either way, how were the South Vietnamese and their allies supposed to trust any peace negotiations with the North and the Viet Cong rebels if they couldn't control their own troops?

December 27, 1966 – Kim Son Valley, South Vietnam

It was 1 AM at Firebase Bird, and most of the troops

of C Battery 6th Battalion, 16th Artillery, and B Battery 2nd Battalion, 19th Artillery were asleep. The gun crew quarters were located next to the gun pit where their howitzer was situated. The understrength C Company from 1st Battalion, 12th Cavalry Regiment, 1st Calvary Division defended the base while the arti guys did their thing protecting the troops on patrol throughout the valley and surrounding mountains. A well-placed artillery strike could break the enemy's will to fight and keep the allied forces from being overrun by the Viet Cong or NVA forces during an ambush or assault on a base.

The two artillery batteries in Firebase Bird's area of operation were in and around the Kim Song Valley. The low-lying hilltop base was located 100 yards from a bend in the meandering Kim Son River that ran through the valley. There was a landing pad for supply and transport helicopters with a 500-gallon fuel bladder off to one side to top off the helicopters' fuel tanks before returning to their air bases. A dozen plus artillery pits were scattered around the hilltop each holding a 105 mm or 155 mm howitzer surrounded by a triple layer of sandbags. There were also multiple machine gun and recoilless rifle emplacements. The Americans had a total of 170 soldiers assigned to the base.

Karen and Simon Bryant had flown in on a supply helicopter the day before. Simon interviewed the commanding officer and several of the troops while Karen snapped shots of whatever she could. There wasn't that much to see. More of an afterthought, the firebase was not their main assignment. They were to embed with a cavalry battalion carrying out a search and destroy mission in the mountains around the valley. But since they were at the firebase, they took advantage of the opportunity to develop an additional story. After eating some dinner and visiting with a few of the soldiers, Karen and Simon sacked out in a tent the base commander had set up for them.

Simon started to snore and woke Karen. She was annoyed until she realized she needed to pee anyway. That was a big problem in Vietnam; she needed to drink a lot of water to keep from becoming dehydrated, but with her bladder being constantly filled to capacity, she had to pee like a fire hydrant. She crawled out of the tent and made her way in the dark to the latrine. Dense clouds covered the moon making it pitch black. There were no lights permitted after dark on the base. The night was Charlie's time, and nobody wanted to give a sniper an opportunity to snuff out his enemy. Better to shuffle one's feet and hope you don't trip in the dark.

After using the rustic facilities, Karen was about to head back to her shared tent, when she noticed something moving in the distance. She let her eyes adjust a bit more and saw that it was not one thing moving but a bunch of things moving toward the slope leading to the hilltop base. In the dark, they looked like an intrusion of cockroaches scampering toward a fallen scrap of food. It occurred to her that she and the American soldiers in the firebase were the food. She wondered why the base's machine guns and recoilless rifles had not opened fire on the approaching wave of enemy soldiers. She reached for her pistol in her shoulder holster. It wasn't there. She had left her holster and weapon in the tent. She looked around for someone to warn about the NVA assault and saw nobody close by. She took another look at the army of cockroaches and saw that they had stopped moving at the base of the hill. Moments later, she discovered the reason…

Right on cue, enemy mortar rounds bombarded the firebase, exploding and sending red-hot shrapnel in all directions. With no cover nearby, Karen dove to the ground. She was petrified as shells exploded around her. She kept waiting for a searing piece of shrapnel to plunge itself into her flesh. She waited for the intense pain that would lead to her death. The flashes from the explosions provided plenty of light and she could see the entire base which was the size of a football field. Soldiers were running to the fire positions; some were cut down in stride by the exploding mortar shells, and others were hurled into the air and landed in heaps. It was horrifying to watch. Karen knew that those soldiers would be the only thing between her and the NVA that were about to assault the hilltop firebase.

After a minute of extensive shelling, Karen decided it was stupid to lie on the ground and wait for her death. She needed to fight back and for that, she needed her pistol. She started belly-crawling back to her tent.

When she reached it and crawled inside, she saw that Simon was gone. She was disappointed and a bit panicked. Simon was a veteran war correspondent and had been in many battles. He gave her confidence that they would survive. She missed him as she grabbed her shoulder harness and slipped it on. She opened her rucksack and dug through it until she found her box of extra bullets. She slid the box into an oversized pocket in the leg of her jumpsuit. At least she could defend herself if the base were overrun. Overrun by the NVA. From the rumors she had heard, she would most likely be raped, she thought. She couldn't let that happen. It would destroy her emotionally. To Karen, that was worse than death.

Grabbing her camera bag, she crawled out of the tent. If she was going to die, she would leave a record of the battle on the film in her camera... a camera that would most likely be plundered by the NVA. There was nothing she could do about that if it happened. She could only do her job and hope for the best. She looked around for signs of Simon. He was nowhere in sight. She hoped he was safe wherever he was. She started taking photos as the explosions lit up the base. She kept the camera's aperture almost closed, fearing that the bright explosions would overexpose her shots. The chaos and death in her viewfinder were palatable. It was what she came to Vietnam to achieve, revealing the horrors of war.

A regiment of NVA had taken advantage of the Christmas ceasefire to move into position around Firebase Bird. They were determined to wipe out the Americans and their artillery. With a total of 1,000 soldiers, the odds were in the favor of the NVA. They outnumber the Americans by over five-to-one and the hillside was shallow. The NVA were already close enough to render the firebase's howitzers useless. The NVA had grabbed the Americans by the belt. Firebase Bird was in deep trouble.

Staff Sergeant Delbert Owen Jennings was in command of a squad from C Company, 1st Battalion, 12th Cavalry Regiment, 1st Air Cavalry Division protecting the firebase. Like most of the soldiers in the firebase, he was asleep when the NVA assault began. The first explosion woke him and the adrenaline pumping through his body quickly cleared the fog of sleep from his head. Almost by instinct, he reached out, grabbed two bandoliers of magazines and his M16 rifle, then his helmet as he leapt from his rack. The rest of his squad was doing the same and headed for the bunker's doorway.

An explosion just outside blew the lead soldier back into the bunker plowing over the other members of the squad like bowling pins. Nobody was hurt but the explosion put an exclamation point on the seriousness of what was waiting outside. Jennings took the lead this time as the squad headed out of the bunker once more.

Shells from recoilless rifles and mortars continued to bombard the firebase as the bursts of light created an eerie strobe effect of the American troops running to their defensive positions. Like Vietnamese shadow puppets, the American soldiers were backlit by the bright flashes as they ran across the hilltop.

Enemy machine-gun fire ripped into the sandbags and earthen mounds protecting the American firing positions and artillery pits. Several enemy mortar rounds hit the communication bunker and destroyed the antae cutting off radio calls for air and artillery support. The nearby American forces knew that Firebase Bird was under heavy attack but could do nothing in the way of artillery support until communications were reestablished and fire coordinates could be relayed. There was far too much risk of hitting their own troops.

As the mortar and recoilless rifle fire subsided, Jennings knew what was about to happen. He missed his M14. It was reliable, and even if the ammunition weighed a lot, he was confident it could pierce the dense jungle where the Viet Cong and NVA were hidden. The M16 he was carrying was a different beast, even with its higher muzzle velocity and lighter weight. Unless kept impeccably clean and frequently oiled, it jammed… a lot. The M16's bullets were supposed to tumble when they hit a leaf or vine, making them more deadly, but Jennings didn't think it made much of a difference. A big bullet was just as capable of killing the enemy as a small, tumbling bullet. He kept looking for a reason that the US Military switched to the M16 but so far hadn't found one. The missing logic pissed him off.

He flipped the rifle's selection switch to full auto. The NVA attacked in human-waves, and he wanted to be ready at a moment's notice. It didn't take long…

The sappers were the first to start up the hill. They used satchel packs of explosives to breach the barbed wire around the firebase perimeter. The Americans set off foo gas barrels hidden in the hillside. The gas fireball launched from the barrel engulfed anyone in its path. Few sappers hit with the burning gas survived.

Once the perimeter was breached by the sappers, the NVA rose from their hidden positions at the bottom of the hill and started the climb as fast as possible. The quicker they could reach the enemy positions the better their chances of survival. Their assault consisted of three lines of formations of 500 soldiers. Like an ocean wave, they crashed over the enemy's position overwhelming the defenders with the sheer weight of the assaulting soldiers. It was a costly tactic, but it did work much of the time.

Jennings and his men opened fire. They poured as much firepower as they were able to drive the approaching enemy to the ground. Jennings ordered the remaining foo gas barrels ignited as the NVA formation approached. Dozens of NVA were consumed by the fireballs and died horrific deaths. Still, the mass of soldiers continued up the hill, firing their rifles as they ascended.

Seeing that they were about to be overrun, Jennings came up with a solution. The helicopter that had landed the night before had dropped off a new case of grenades that had not been unpacked yet. Jennings ordered three of his men to remove the grenades from the protective sleeves, straighten the pins, then toss them to him one at a time. As each grenade became ready, Jennings pulled the safety ring at the end of the pin, allowed the lever to fling away, then hurled the grenade down the slope at the approaching NVA.

Dozens of exploding grenades took their toll on the NVA's front-line soldiers. But it still wasn't enough.

As the crate of grenades ran low, Jennings considered his next move. He knew that his squad alone could not stop the advancing NVA. The safety of his men was paramount in his mind. Just before the first formation of NVA reached the crest of the hill, Jennings ordered his men to retreat back into the firebase where more Americans were fighting. Jennings stayed behind to keep up the fire on the enemy covering his squad's withdrawal. Jennings killed twelve more NVA with his rifle before leaving his position overlooking the hillside and rejoining his men. On his way, he encountered three sappers attempting to blow up one of the American howitzers. Jennings opened fire with his M16 killing all three. He killed three more enemy soldiers emerging from the squad's bunker that they had just invaded. Jennings was not thinking about what he was doing. He didn't calculate the odds of his actions. He had let his instinct and training take over and kept killing any enemy he found as he retreated back into the firebase. He killed one enemy soldier with the butt of his rifle smashing the man's skull as he passed.

A secondary enemy assault to the southeast began with sappers once again taking out the perimeter barbed wire with their satchel charges and the Americans igniting their foo gas barrels. A second battalion of NVA started up the hill and was met with heavy gunfire from the surviving American soldiers on that side of the firebase.

When he finally rejoined his men, Jennings was informed that eight seriously wounded men were still at the edge of the hillside that the enemy was now pouring over. He asked for volunteers and set out to rescue the men. Keeping out of the way of the main fighting effort, Jennings and his volunteers made their way behind several gun pits using the sandbags to cover their movements. Jennings and the volunteers disregarded their own safety and braved boobytraps and sniper fire as they advanced. When they finally reached the position of the eight wounded men, eight of the volunteers carried the wounded men in fireman's carries, while Jennings and two other volunteers covered their rescue with their rifles and grenades. All the volunteers and wounded soldiers made it back to the American lines. Miraculously unharmed, Jennings and the two volunteers arrived a few minutes later.

By the time Jennings had rejoined his squad, most of the gun pits had been overrun and the NVA were using the sandbags around each pit's perimeter as cover to lay down fire on the surviving Americans. Bodies from both sides were strewn across the hilltop.

Some wounded were trying to crawl back to their lines. It was beyond sad as the wounded were picked off by their enemy raising an already high death toll on both sides of the conflict.

The Americans fought back several NVA assaults coming from two sides of the hilltop as the communists attempted to overrun the final holdout position on the opposite edge of the hilltop where the assault had originated. The American commander of Firebase Bird, Lieutenant Colonel Baker, had called for air support, but it was still ten minutes out. When radio communications were reestablished, Firebase Pony on the opposite end of the valley was radioed and provided artillery support that took its toll on the NVA, but it wasn't able to stop them. With his executive officer already dead, Baker turned to his NCO assistant, commander Sergeant Major Philips, and said, "How many men do we have that can still fight?"

"I'm not sure, sir. Maybe seventy," said Philips. "Whatever it is, it ain't enough. They're gonna overrun us eventually. Maybe this next wave."

"I agree. Crank one of the howitzers to maximum elevation and launch a green flare over the firebase, then set the remaining howitzers to Zero Point and have the gunners load APERS-T rounds."

"Yes, sir. Sir?"

"Yes, sergeant?"

"Beehive rounds? We still have men out there, sir."

"I am well aware of that, Sergeant. But this base is gonna fall unless we do something fast. I can't let that happen."

"Green flare, then beehive rounds. Will do, sir."

The sergeant moved off to execute his

commander's orders. Two minutes later, a howitzer pointing almost straight up, fired a green starshell flare that arced across the sky over the firebase, then ejected its parachute, and floated downward illuminating everything in a green ghostly light.

The APERS-T anti-personnel shell nicknamed the Beehive round was a 105 mm howitzer direct-fire round that had never been fired in combat. It was designed to fend off human-wave-type attacks similar to a canister shell but far more deadly. The Beehive shell contained 8,000 metal flechettes packed in high explosives. The flechettes were fin-stabilized projectiles the size of a nail fired at a high velocity. When they came in contact with bone, the flechettes would usually bend into a hook while the fins break off and continue their flight at different angles creating additional projectiles as they leave the enemy's body. The nickname Beehive round came from the appearance of the flechettes packed into the shell like a beehive. The fuse was usually set to go off as the round leaves the barrel of the howitzer. The Beehive was devastatingly effective against exposed infantry.

Caught between the American and NVA lines, Karen was still searching for Bryant. She feared the worst. She was using whatever cover she could find to hide her movements. It occurred to her that she was just as likely to be shot by an American as an NVA. She stuck to the shadows and crawled on the ground whenever possible. She heard the pop of the starshell in the sky above the hilltop and watched the green flare descend on a parachute. She didn't know what it meant.

She heard a "PSSST," and turned to see Bryant twenty yards away, kneeling by a bunker. She smiled.

She was really glad to see him. He motioned toward the American lines. She nodded, then turned back to see if the coast was clear. It wasn't. Hundreds of NVA soldiers were appearing from behind hidden positions. It was the final attack. Karen froze in fear. Bryant saw her and knew right away she was in trouble. He also saw the NVA running across the hilltop. They would reach Karen in less than a minute. Bryant sprung from his covered position behind the bunker and ran for Karen. Karen saw him and whispered to herself, "No."

It was too late. Bryant was hit in his left thigh by a machine-gun burst and went down like a sack of potatoes. He groaned in pain grabbing the wound. Karen knew it was her fault. She sprang from cover and ran toward him. Bryant tried to wave her off, but she wouldn't stop. She slid next to him like a baseball player sliding into second. She pulled off his belt and cinched it tight around his leg to slow the bleeding. She turned back to see the NVA closing on their position, firing their rifles. "We gotta go," said Karen.

"No shit," said Bryant. "Help me to my feet then take off running."

"I'm not leaving you," said Karen helping him stand.

"Then we're both gonna die."

"Yeah. Probably. But I'm still not leaving you."

They started moving toward the American lines, Karen acting like a crutch, helping Bryant hop across the hilltop. Karen yelled to the Americans hoping they didn't shoot her and Bryant.

The remaining howitzer was lowered to Zero Point, almost parallel to the ground and a beehive round was loaded, the breach slamming shut. Baker looked out at the hilltop and saw Karen and Bryant hobbling toward the American position, in the fire path of the howitzer, the wave of NVA running toward them in the distance, and said, "Goddammit. Sergeant, send some of your men to—"

Before Baker could finish his sentence, Philips jumped over the sandbags and ran toward Karen and Bryant. He knew what needed to be done and that there was no time to give orders. He just did it.

As Philips reached them, he grabbed Bryant and threw him over his shoulder in a fireman's carry, then said to Karen, "Run, dammit!"

"I'm not leaving him," said Karen grabbing onto Bryant's arm and trying to pull him toward the American lines.

"Run, or I'm gonna put my boot up your ass, you dumb broad!"

Karen believed him, releasing Bryant's hand, and ran for the American lines as enemy bullets zinged past her head while some bounced off the ground with puffs of dirt. Ten seconds later, she jumped over the sandbags and watch as the sergeant huffed and puffed his way toward the lines. It was all her fault; she was the reason that Bryant and the brave sergeant were going to die. It was her fault the Americans were going to be overrun. She looked at the mass of enemy troops running toward her and felt alone and helpless. She sat down with her back to the sandbags, pulled out her pistol, and put it to her temple. She realized she could miss her brain and just mess up her looks with a big scar. She moved the barrel to under her chin. Better. No missing her brain this way. Tears ran down her cheeks as she prepared herself. There wasn't much time. She felt a hand on top of hers pushing the barrel away. It was the firebase commander. Baker said, "Not yet. Give us one more chance. I'll tell you when it's time. Okay?"

Karen nodded and lowered the gun to her lap. Baker watched as the NVA closed to within 100 feet of the American position and said, "Sergeant Philips, down!"

Philips and Bryant were still short of the sandbags but had run out of time. Philips used all his remaining strength to push Bryant towards the sandbag and dove to the ground. The howitzer fired with a deafening roar. The beehive shell left the barrel and ignited the high explosives launching the 8,000 flechettes toward the enemy.

The middle of the NVA line disappeared in a red mist as dozens of soldiers were ripped to shreds by the little metal arrows. But more arrows made it through the bodies in the front line and continued forward hitting the second and third line killing more and more soldiers. Almost one hundred NVA soldiers were killed with one round. The NVA watching their comrades die were in shock. Their advance faltered.

The Americans continued to fire on the NVA as the howitzer gun crew loaded a second beehive round. The barrel was shifted slightly to one side and the weapon was again fired.

Another eighty NVA were killed in a most gruesome manner, torn apart by an invisible force. The surviving NVA were terrified and broke, running back toward the edge of the hilltop.

Another round was loaded into the howitzer. Philips lifted Bryant over the sandbags and dropped him on the ground. Bryant groaned loudly. Karen crawled over and cradled Bryant in her arms. Philips crawled over the sandbags himself and pointed to the southeastern side of the hilltop and said, "They're coming."

Baker turned and saw another NVA battalion appearing over the edge of the hilltop from a different angle. He ordered the howitzer redirected toward the new threat. It was aimed down the American line. Philips shouted, "You men get the fuck out of the way!"

Seeing what was about to happen the Americans on that side of the line crawled away from the line of fire. Now that the firing line was clear, Baker gave the order to fire. The howitzer roared again.

Fifty NVA climbing over the edge of the hilltop disintegrated, some decapitated. It was a horrific scene. Seeing the red mist that was once their comrades, the NVA climbing the slope turned and ran back down the slope.

Huey and Chinook gunships finally arrived, rocketing and strafing the retreating NVA. The NVA kept running and didn't stop even when they reached the edge of the jungle. They were horrified by what they had witnessed on the hilltop.

Baker turned to Karen and said with a shrug, "See."

Karen stayed by Bryant's side as he was evacuated by helicopter to a military hospital at a nearby air base. She was alive and grateful for it. She knew she was changing, but she wasn't sure how. She felt more afraid than ever, but also felt the thrill of almost being killed and in a strange way… liked it.

It wasn't a victory, but the surviving Americans held their position, and it was the NVA that retreated. With twenty-seven killed in action and sixty-seven wounded, sixty percent of the American soldier on Firebase Bird were casualties. The NVA losses were 267 dead and countless wounded. For his heroic actions during the assault on Firebase Bird, Staff Sergeant Jennings was awarded the Medal of Honor.

By the end of 1966, 485,300 American soldiers were fighting in Vietnam and Laos. 6,350 had been killed in action. The South Vietnamese had 735,900 soldiers in uniform of which 11,953 had been killed during the year. South Korea had 45,566 soldiers in-country while the rest of the remaining allied forces from Thailand, Australia, New Zealand, and the Philippines numbered 6,985 combined. It was estimated that the Viet Cong and NVA numbered 282,000 with an unknown number of killed and wounded. CIA analysts were cynical at the low number and gave their own estimate of over 600,000 communist soldiers fighting against the allied forces. It seemed there was no stopping the juggernaut called, "The Vietnam War."

LETTER TO THE READER

Dear Reader,

I hoped you enjoyed Beyond Courage. I was certainly excited when writing it and humbled by the incredible sacrifices and bravery of the soldiers fighting in the war.

The next book in the Airmen Series will be Flames of War which will cover the explosive year of 1967. After a year of building bases and troops arriving in country, General Westmoreland believed that the American military was ready for major offensives against the Viet Cong and North Vietnamese forces. However, the communist forces had also carried out their own buildup of weapons and troops in the south. They too were chomping at the bit to get at the enemy. It was going to be one hell of a year for both sides.

I appreciate you reading my stories. You give them meaning. I look forward to hearing from you.

Sincerely,

David Lee Corley

LIST OF TITLES WITH READING ORDER

The Airmen Series

1. A War Too Far
2. The War Before The War
3. We Stand Alone
4. Café Wars
5. Sèvres Protocol
6. Operation Musketeer
7. Battle of The Casbah
8. Momentum of War
9. The Willful Slaughter of Hope
10. Kennedy's War
11. The Uncivil War
12. Cry Havoc
13. When War Dawns
14. A Savage Joy
15. Beyond Courage
16. Flames of War

The Nomad Series

1. Monsoon Rising
2. Prophecies of Chaos
3. Stealing Thunder

Facebook Page:
https://www.facebook.com/historicalwarnovels

Shopify Store: https://david-lee-corley.myshopify.com/

Amazon Author's Page:
https://www.amazon.com/David-Lee-Corley/e/B073S1ZMWQ

Amazon Airmen Series Page:
https://www.amazon.com/dp/B07JVRXRGG

Amazon Nomad Series Page:
https://www.amazon.com/dp/B07CKFGQ95

Author's Website: http://davidleecorley.com/

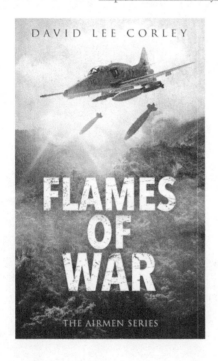

AUTHOR'S BIOGRAPHY

Born in 1958, David grew up on a horse ranch in Northern California, breeding and training appaloosas. He has had all his toes broken at least once and survived numerous falls and kicks from ornery colts and fillies. David started writing professionally as a copywriter in his early 20's. At 32, he packed up his family and moved to Malibu, California, to live his dream of writing and directing motion pictures. He has four motion picture screenwriting credits and two directing credits. His movies have been viewed by over 50 million movie-goers worldwide and won a multitude of awards, including the Malibu, Palm Springs, and San Jose Film Festivals. In addition to his 24 screenplays, he has written fourteen novels. He developed his simplistic writing style after rereading his two favorite books, Ernest Hemingway's "The Old Man and The Sea" and Cormac McCarthy's "No Country For Old Men." An avid student of world culture, David lived as an expat in both Thailand and Mexico. At 56, he sold all his possessions and became a nomad for four years. He circumnavigated the globe three times and visited 56 countries. Known for his detailed descriptions, his stories often include actual experiences and characters from his journeys.

Made in United States
North Haven, CT
14 September 2024